BACK
FROM THE
BRINK
Too

© Bird In Hand Media

Published by Bird In Hand Media
P.O. Box 278, Gordon NSW 2072

Distributed in Australia by Gary Allen
For further information about orders
Phone: +61 2 9725 2933
Email: customerservice@garyallen.com.au

National Library of Australia Cataloguing-in-Publication Data:

Cowan, Graeme
Back from the Brink Too: helping your loved one in overcoming depression.
1st ed. ISBN 9 7 809803393 1 4 (paperback)
Cowan, Graeme. 1. Depression, mental. 2 Self help.
    616.8527

Project managed by Messenger Publishing
www.messengerpublishing.com.au
Design: Messenger Publishing
Editing: Anna Crago, Messenger Publishing
Cover image: iStock
Printed in China

BACK
FROM THE
BRINK *Too*

Helping your loved one
OVERCOME DEPRESSION

bird in hand
m e d i a

To my children, Melissa and Adam, who were my motivation to keep trying, even when things seemed hopeless.

Support for Back from the Brink Too

'If only all carers of people with depression could read this useful, informative book, and find out that they are not alone! With first-hand accounts and advice about caring, and importantly about self-care, this book is a must! Thank you Graeme for writing this book.'

Elena Katrakis, CEO, Carers NSW

'This book goes to the heart of how individuals can care for someone with depression. It also comes from the heart – of someone who has walked the journey and can define how caregivers can best "care".'

Professor Gordon Parker, Executive Director, Blackdog Institute

'This book has many valuable insights into the impact of depression on families, and practical information on how to address the needs of carers.'

Warren Jenkins, Executive Director, ARAFEMI Victoria

'This book is complementary to the extensive beyondblue research; it highlights not only the challenges for those supporting someone with depression, but also the profound impact it can have on their own wellbeing. By giving valuable insight into people's experiences and providing useful strategies this book can assist carers and family members to not only help those with depression, but importantly also help themselves.'

Jeff Kennett AC, Chairman, beyondblue: the national depression initiative

'Family members of people with mental illness play an enormous role in providing care and support for relatives experiencing the pain and distress of depression - too often without the support and education they need themselves. Back from the Brink Too will be of immense value to the hundreds of thousands of Australians in this situation.
'A recurring underlying theme from family members who call SANE's Helpline is that they feel alone and that others don't understand what they are going through. Hearing from others in a similar situation in Back from the Brink Too, will provide readers with reassurance that they are not alone, that there is support out there and that there are ways in which they can help their relative manage or even overcome their depression.'

Barbara Hocking, Executive Director, SANE Australia

'I wish I could have put my hand on 'Back to the Brink Too' a few decades ago! This is a superbly researched and deeply moving anthology of hope and inspiration. Finally the greatly overdue and needed voice of Carers can be heard as they speak to us openly about loving and living with a dear one battling depression and anxiety. What comes with the role of Carer places them very much at risk of becoming unwell themselves. 'These pages offer comfort and connectedness, filling an enormous void that will make a profound difference to those spirits negotiating the often confronting and complex path of life as a Carer. Congratulations on this outstanding work.'

Ingrid Ozols, Managing Director, mh@work®, mentalhealth@work

'Carers are the unsung heroes of our society. I know from research that I have conducted and from speaking to many individual carers over the years that a person with mental illness who has a carer is far more likely to have a good quality of life and be able to achieve recovery.'

'Back from the Brink Too offers sound advice and support to carers in an easy to read and understand format. The factual information and first hand accounts contained in this book provide a conduit to gaining the knowledge and support which will assist them to not only care for their loved one but also for themselves. Back from the Brink Too will both change and enhance the lives of the many people who will read it.'

Bernard McNair RN, Foundation Director Mental Health Council of Australia

Support for Back from the Brink — Australians Tell Their Stories of Overcoming Depression

'This book is brave, uplifting, informative, inspirational and optimistic … anything but depressing.'

Good Reading Magazine, Nov 2007

'These first hand accounts showing how people have overcome depression are sorely needed. To read about how others have tried various strategies that have ultimately lead to recovery, gives hope and inspiration.'

Ms Dawn Smith, CEO, Lifeline Australia

'Depression is one of the most prevalent conditions our 25000 General Practitioners from around Australia encounter. Graeme's book will help our members explain to their patients that people from all walks of life can be affected. It contains very courageous testimonies and research which will benefit both our doctors and their patients.'

Ms Kate Carnell, CEO, Australian General Practice Network

Contents

About the author

Who is Graeme Cowan?

WITHOUT PUTTING TOO fine a point on it, I would not be here today without the care and support of my parents, and my then wife Susan, during my bouts with depression.

From the outside, it looked like I had a successful life. It was 1989 and I was married and had a beautiful one-year-old daughter and a close extended family. My career had progressed well; first in marketing, and then in human resources. But behind this, I had privately been battling depression since I was 21. Not all the time – but regularly.

After a particularly disabling episode, I attempted suicide. I was 31. At that time it's fair to say that I didn't even really know what depression was, and when the doctor told me that he wanted to admit me to a psychiatric hospital, my shame knew no bounds. I made my wife promise to only tell my parents about my admission – under no circumstances was she to tell ANYONE about the suicide attempt.

I can only begin now to understand the stress that must have placed on her. Not only was she looking after our young daughter, working part-time, and managing the household; she also had to pretend that everything was normal. She had to tell lies to cover for her husband in hospital. The load was enormous. To make matters worse, back then, depression wasn't spoken about, and there were very few resources and support.

Thanks to medication, I responded quite quickly to treatment and was back at work and 'normal' again fairly soon.

THINGS WENT WELL for a long time, until 2000. At the time I was Joint Managing Director of an executive search firm. I began a five-year episode which my psychiatrist described as the worst he had ever treated. During that time I tried 23 medications, had ECT or shock therapy on 20 occasions, was hospitalised four times, tried transcranial magnetic stimulation, kinesiology, acupuncture, and counselling. I also lost my job. At this point Susan decided for her own sanity and that of the children that she couldn't support me any longer. I now know that during that time I was not sharing my load as a parent. Now, I can understand why she made that decision – but at the time it seemed like another nail in my coffin.

By this stage I was incapable of looking after myself, and thankfully my parents took me in. They supported and believed in me when I had lost hope. Eventually, in utter despair, I made another attempt on my own life. Still, they hung in there relentlessly. My siblings also tried as best they could to help. I was with my parents for 18 months and I can't imagine how difficult it must have been for them.

Eventually I did make substantial progress. In time, I moved out by myself and wrote the bestseller *Back from the Brink: Australians tell their stories of overcoming depression*. For those interested in my full story of decline and recovery, it can be found in *Back from the Brink* or for free at www.IamBackFromTheBrink.com. I only mention part of my story here so that readers understand what led me to write a book about overcoming depression.

Back from the Brink turned out to meet a real need in the market. Before I started the writing I interviewed over 300 people with depression to understand exactly who they would like to see in the book and what they would like me to ask them. It contained inspiring stories of prominent and everyday Australians who had fought depression and gone on to make great contributions in life. It was these raw stories, I realised, which really resonated with people.

Back from the Brink, Too is not a book about me or those living with depression. It is a book dedicated to those brave, unheralded souls who support those of us living with depression.

It is estimated that for every person with depression, there are at least two carers supporting them. In Australia that means there are two million people caring for a loved one with depression. Their contribution is immense, but largely invisible. I really only began to understand how large this hidden army was after the release of *Back from the Brink*. At least 50 per cent of the people that attended my book signings and responded to my appearances on talk-back radio were carers. Many were at their wits' end, struggling to help their loved one while also trying to keep their own head above water.

As I had done with *Back from the Brink*, I did extensive research. This time around, I wanted to try and understand the problems that carers were experiencing. I wanted to find out what questions they desperately wanted answered. And so I interviewed 289 carers of people with depression.

I was humbled by their frankness and probably for the first time began to understand the strain my parents and my former wife had been under. One particular woman who responded took my breath away. On 13 June 2007, she heard John Brogden and I on Radio National discussing the launch of *Back from the Brink*. On that same day, her beautiful daughter took her own life. She encouraged me to get *Back from the Brink, Too* out there – it was desperately needed, she said. Despite her attempts to get help, she told me, she had found it incredibly hard to get the answers she needed in order to be able to support her daughter. She told me that carers' involvement and feedback was rarely requested by mental health professionals (often, supposedly, for privacy reasons). This philosophy is, at best, counterproductive and, at worst, bordering on negligence.

In addition to the carers I spoke with, I also interviewed over 300 people living with depression. I asked them how they would like to be supported, and what they would like to say to their caregivers.

Having had the chance to now see things from both perspectives – that of the person living with depression and that of the carer – I am totally convinced that both parties have to work closely in partnership to beat the black dog.

The other thing I know for sure is that caregivers must not let their own health deteriorate as they care for their depressed loved one. According to research done for this book, 81 per cent of caregivers have had either their mental or physical health adversely affected by the caring role.

The objectives of this book are to provide you with the information to best help your loved one with depression, AND to provide you with resources to help yourself and ensure you don't sacrifice your own wellbeing.

In Australia, the people who support an ill loved one are often referred to as carers. While I can relate to that term, I feel it implies that is all they do. In reality, they also have many other roles – parent, employee, friend, community contributor and so forth. In the US, interestingly, the term caregiver is used for the same role. To me this implies that caring for a loved one is just one thing that they do. In this book we have applied the terms carer and caregiver equally, as I feel they each contribute to the understanding of the role.

I have been lucky to have worked closely with a US-based researcher and writer, Jacqueline Hampton, in preparing this book. We have tried to access the best resources and answers from Australia, the US, and around the world. Quite frankly, carers deserve this. The information is often out there but it takes tenacity and diligence to bring it all together and I thank Jacqueline for her role in making this happen.

I would also like to sincerely thank Nerida Egan and 'Richard' for their invaluable first-hand accounts of being a carer. While facts and figures are helpful, as I discovered with *Back from the Brink*, it is real stories that move the heart. I know that their generosity and willingness to share the good and the bad will be of enormous benefit to many readers.

To my carers when I was in need, Alan and Judy Cowan and Susan; this book is my token of appreciation. I am so grateful that their care allowed me to recover and watch my two beautiful children, Melissa and Adam, grow up.

YOU ARE DOING an amazing and important thing – caring for someone who desperately needs it. Even though at times you may feel unappreciated, you need to know in your heart that you are making a HUGE difference to your loved one. Often they don't know how to express it, but I can assure you that you are.

Congratulations on showing the commitment to read this book in addition to all your other tasks. My sincere hope is that this book contributes to you, the carer, not feeling so alone; and that it answers most of the questions you have ever asked. I also hope that you have clearly got the message that you need to look after yourself – you are no good to anyone if you are sick!

Ultimately I hope that you can one day say that 'I came back from the brink too'.

May the best in life and love and happiness be ahead of you and your loved one.

Graeme Cowan

Foreword

Foreword

Surviving your partner's depression

FOLLOWING ARE A few words of advice on surviving your partner's depression, based on my own experience. The following tips for partners of people with depression were written long before Graeme had thought of writing this second book. They developed from my own need to consider what lessons I had learned from my experience of living with a partner suffering with depression. I had no idea how this list might be used, or if indeed anyone else would ever read it, but now there appears an opportunity to share a perspective that I hope may offer some help to others in the same situation. I didn't know any of these things when we first encountered the life-altering experience of depression in our family, but I wish I had.

1. Don't try to own it

Your partner's depression belongs to them. It is not yours. Help them – yes. Support them – yes. But don't take it on as if it was yours. It won't help either of you.

2. Don't feel guilty for being happy

Depression doesn't have to be contagious. It's okay for you to feel happy when your partner is depressed. You don't have to pretend that you agree with their view of the world. Laugh often – you will need it!

3. Nurture yourself

A depressed partner is incapable of providing you with emotional nourishment. They might want to, but you have to accept that they are just incapable of doing so during a depressive episode. That doesn't mean you have to become malnourished. Nurture yourself – do things you love, be kind to yourself, exercise, eat well, have a drink, relax, read, go to a movie, shop, play.

4. Nurture your children

The reality is that you need to compensate for your partner's inability to parent your children when they are depressed. You have to show your children that you are still a fully-functioning human being, and that they have one parent they can count on to be there for them. Be strong so that they can feel secure. Try to keep their world intact as much as possible.

5. Don't let the depression isolate you

A depressed person doesn't want social interaction. It is difficult for them and often very painful. That doesn't mean you have to cut yourself off from the world to accommodate their withdrawal. In fact, you've never needed support from family and friends as much as you do when your partner is depressed. Unfortunately, at least until very recently, it has been a hidden affliction that sufferers and their partners didn't seek enough support for. If your partner had cancer, people would be dropping in dinners and minding the children for you. Reach out, and you will be overwhelmed by people's kindness and concern.

6. Don't think it is your fault

Your partner's depression comes from within themselves, for reasons most of us can't understand. You didn't cause it. The fight you had didn't cause it. And here is the hard part – you can't fix it either. The cure has to come from within your partner, just as the depression did.

7. Love them even when they can't love you back

A depressed person is totally self-absorbed and incapable of caring much about anyone else. The best thing you can do is let them know they are still loved

– but don't expect anything in return while they are depressed. This is a very hard part of living with a depressed partner. It usually means no emotional connection and probably no physical intimacy, so you will feel very lonely. That's why points 3 and 5 above are so important.

8. Know that this will pass

Your partner will have lost belief that the hell they are going through will end. That is what leads to suicide attempts in the worst cases. Remember you are outside the depression, and you have the clarity to see that it is a stage of their life that will pass. The fog will lift, and they can be happy again. There are countless examples to prove this. Believe it and hang on to the knowledge that it is true.

9. Discover what you are learning

Your partner's depression can actually be a positive thing for you. That sounds strange, but it depends how you look at it. A wise friend listened to my tale of woe about my partner's depression ruining our lives, and asked me 'How is this serving you?' To my utter amazement, I could name several ways I was benefiting from the experience.

You may learn how much inner strength you actually have; you may realise what an inherently optimistic person you are; you may become a leader in the family; you may develop levels of empathy for others you never had before; you may rediscover your independence; you may strengthen your ties with your parents, siblings and friends. You will certainly reassess what really matters in life.

Susan
28 March 2007

Surviving your son's depression

OUR PRIDE AND admiration for our son has never been greater than with the writing of his book *Back from the Brink*. In one of his most difficult times I'd said 'You are going to get through this, and because you have experienced this "black hole", you'll be able to reach others, to show how to get out'. Never did I dream he would write a book.

'Graeme – even the tall, secure, successful, need love and tender care.' – an entry in my diary.

Alan had just retired and we were on a weekend retreat given to us by our kids. Graeme wanted us to spend time apart, and together, to think and write down our goals and plans for this next stage in our lives. When I came to 'family', I'd identified each of the other four children's need for our assistance, but Graeme's were recorded as above.

'Love and tender care' – I remember questioning my words. Never did I realise this would play a part in our retirement. When the time came for him to live with us, I remember thinking, 'What a privilege to care for our son – a grown man – very few parents have this opportunity'.

Childhood

WHAT A JOY, Graeme's arrival in this world – our beautiful son, our first child. He was strong, healthy, and reached milestones early. He succeeded at school, sport, had lots of friends. He was always a leader; his peers looked up to him.

As a 10-year-old, he joined his father, an Apexian, in a walkathon to raise money for the establishment of a blood bank at the local hospital. Graeme, wearing thongs, led the walkers all the way from Coopernook to Taree, a distance of about 20 kilometres.

He loved sport – athletics, swimming, cricket and football. He captained the school football and cricket teams. He was a school prefect, had a lovely girlfriend and great friends. When he left home we felt that we were sending off into the world a young man who would live a happy life.

THEN, IN 1989, Graeme's wife Susan rang us in tears to say Graeme had had a breakdown and was in a psychiatric hospital. We were stunned. (Susan, at Graeme's insistence, did not tell us of his suicide attempt, so we didn't know the worst of it.)

We couldn't comprehend it. Our son, with his career going so well; a lovely wife, a baby, a home – he was secure, successful. How? Why? We rushed down to Sydney.

Graeme was in tears. 'I don't know why I am like this.'

We had no idea about depression, but we were told that we must not tell anyone – it would be detrimental to his work, etc. The story must be 'He has a severe virus'.

We were able to support Susan and the family, and Graeme in hospital. With medication he did respond quickly and was able to return to work. We thought and hoped it was a one-off episode.

Still, we asked ourselves *why*? Were we over-zealous parents? We certainly had been proud of his achievements, supported him with every endeavour he undertook. He was a role model for his siblings and peers – family was a priority in his life. Did we expect too much? Was it a chemical imbalance in the brain? Was it genetic? We were unable to find any history of depression in either of our families.

As we questioned ourselves, Graeme was struggling. Each time he was back on track, striving, achieving higher goals, a downturn would come.

Graeme didn't want us to talk about it widely, although we were able to share with our family. Their support was invaluable. Susan had the additional anxiety of living with Graeme's depression and keeping the children's lives, activities and home and school commitments as normal as possible. It was an enormous strain on her.

Soon he told us they were separating. The effect on Graeme was huge: he felt it was yet another 'failure'. He came to live with us.

Our role was to support him and let him know he was loved, wanted and needed. We tried to think what to do, where to go, who could give guidance. We found our GP to be wonderful. Graeme's psychiatrist in Sydney was also a great source of support and encouragement for us, but we really needed counselling where we lived. Other than that, we tried to keep him busy with physical activities, exercise, swimming, golf, outings of interest, and other ways of involving him: gardening, home tasks, shopping, church groups, socialising, reading papers and books.

Then we searched for voluntary work for him – this did, to some extent, help.

'Still, w

ourselves w

over-zealous

we expect

e asked
y? Were we
parents? Did
oo much?'

Our faith in God was our rock (mostly). There were nights I buried my tears in the pillow – remembering our son's interest in life before – his great smile, the way he was a real 'people's man'. He never was a 'chatty' man, but participated fully in discussions and conversations, enjoyed jokes, had a great sense of humour, and always provided great support for those in need. Now we found him quiet and not able to communicate very well; he was almost impossible to reach at times.

We learned to ask how he was feeling on a scale from 1 to 10. This was a great way for him to express how he felt and easy for us to understand. When he was below 5, we should have taken it more seriously, and acted.

We were always on the alert for anyone with experience about depression. We read books and articles. Graeme and Alan once travelled 800 kilometres to see the psychologist and author Dorothy Rowe talk. It was helpful knowing there were thousands of people suffering with depression.

Graeme contacted a support group called GROW and joined a local group. This was good for him – finally he felt able to share how he was feeling, and also hear from others in the same situation.

HOW DID WE cope? It was a very difficult time for us, with other family difficulties and sadness going on behind the scenes as well. All the time we had tried to keep up our regular activities – family, church, community, exercise, Better Hearing tutoring, golf, Rotary and Probus.

We longed to communicate with other carers who were also struggling. But at the time, the stigma of depression was too great; he still didn't want us to talk about it. But how helpful it would have been to have been able to ask others: how was/is it for you?

DO YOU WANT to end your life? This was one question we did not ask. We should have. Lifeline is very definite on this.

We knew he was with us; we thought we could protect him. WRONG. Although he seemed to be improving, and was interested in the computer course he was taking, Graeme took an overdose whilst we were away on a day trip. We found him unconscious. Luckily a friend who was a nurse was with us, and helped us follow instructions from emergency services while we waited for the ambulance. It was so comforting at such a stressful time. Alan accompanied Graeme in the ambulance. Our GP was at the hospital. We cannot ever forget how supporting and caring he was. He reassured us about Graeme's chances of recovery and stayed with us for a considerable time.

Graeme regained consciousness the next afternoon with all the family around his bed.

It was a long journey back. Despite all the mental health professionals – psychologists! psychiatrists! mental health team! – we were always amazed that no one wanted to talk with the carers (us!), even though we had asked.

A psychologist we saw advised us to talk to Graeme about his attempted suicide but we found it a very difficult subject to raise.

The family came up from Sydney in shifts to help. His sister did a lot of research and was able to find a visiting psychologist from Sydney, whom Graeme related with well. He saw Graeme regularly and set further stepping stones in place.

Eventually he felt the need to return to Sydney to be near his children, and found a great volunteer job, which involved using his interviewing skills. However at the same time, he was struggling with divorce and financial settlements which had a huge impact on his life. He needed to make sure he could have enough loving contact with his children, be included in their lives. We knew and understood the toll this was taking.

All this led to the depression cycle starting again. Again he was hospitalised, and again his progress was slow. We had the opportunity to attend a carer workshop with a psychologist, which was very helpful. Gradually, he started to improve, with new medication and regular exercise. Then an old school friend who he had met again at a school reunion reached out to Graeme. She had been through depression herself, and understood what it was like. They began a relationship, which really helped with his recovery. He also began to meet others who had experienced depression and understood the isolation and the lack of self-esteem. What a relief and joy for us. He began to further and deepen his meditation practice. With this he has found a wonderful means to inner peace and joy. He started to feel better about himself.

Then the first book – what a triumph!

OUR FAMILY AND close friends have been a wonderful support and we could not have done it without each other.

We wish others who are now in the situation we have just described our love and respect. It is a difficult journey but it can have a happy ending. Our advice is: don't do it alone. Reach out to others. Take heart from this book and know you are not the only one. Read it carefully. Underline sections that resonate. Read it again when you are struggling.

We are so proud that Graeme has acknowledged the role of carers – their journeys and their needs – in writing *Back from the Brink Too*.

With love
Alan and Judy Cowan

Entering the
Black Hole

Entering the Black Hole

DOES THIS SOUND familiar?

You are a caregiver to a depressed loved one. It could be your partner, a sibling, your child, your parent or a friend. And you are helping, doing a good thing.

Doing the right thing.

But things have started to feel vaguely wrong somehow, lately. Not 'sky is falling' wrong or anything. More like an uneasy sense that much of what you used to be able to count on no longer seems to make any sense. Your intuition seems slightly off but for the life of you, you cannot put your finger on what's changed. 'It's just depression, after all,' you tell yourself. It's not like your loved one has cancer or anything.

You are a bit taken aback to find yourself more irritable lately. Things that you used to take in stride bug you now. You find your feelings escalating into anger more often. This realisation gives way to a staggering wave of shame. Feeling angry doesn't fit your image of a caregiver. Mother Teresa, right? How far are you from that when you're angry?

Then the guilt hits. Like you needed that! It's hard enough to figure out the best way to respond to the ups and downs your loved one is experiencing, let alone have to deal with your own emotional juggernaut.

Worse still, you're noticing that people outside your relationship are starting to treat you as if you were the one with … the problem. You think, 'But I'm okay, right?' Then you feel angry all over again. How could they know anything about your situation, anyway? How annoying.

The truth is, the way people are treating you is starting to make you feel a little lonely and isolated. Where is your support system? Your loved one used to be a great support. Now they have their hands full dealing with their depression. To your surprise, some of the people you thought you could count on are tired of hearing about it. They don't get why your family member or friend can't just snap out of it. You don't get how they could ignore someone who needs help. Now you feel guilty all over again for feeling self-righteous.

You're starting to feel worn out. It's not at all what you'd planned for your life. The vibrant palette of living seems to have paled and all of the colours run into a thin, endless stream of beige. There is no relief in sight, yet you soldier on.

You desperately want to help your loved one get better.

Based on what everyone has always said – church, school, your parents, the media – being a caregiver is rising to the noblest calling – helping a fellow human in need. But to you it is starting to feel a lot less like basking in the shining light of compassion and quite a bit more like falling into a big black hole yourself. You aren't riding in on a white horse to save anybody. More like you are being dragged along behind it.

Does this scenario sound at all familiar to you? If you are the caregiver for a depressed loved one, chances are it does. But don't worry; help is at hand.

Please take heart

I was truly surprised that at least 50 per cent of the people that came to my book signings for *Back from the Brink* were caregivers who told me they were experiencing some form of the isolation and frustration I've just outlined. They feel invisible and vulnerable and don't know where to turn. I also know that half of the people that contact Beyondblue – Australia's national depression initiative – are caregivers seeking advice and insight into what they should do.

Research shows that for every person with depression, there are at least two carers. You are part of a large group, and you are crucial to your loved one's recovery. And yet many people with depression ask their caregivers to keep their role secret because of the stigma associated with depression, which can make things doubly hard.

First and foremost, depression is an illness. If your loved one had cancer or dementia, your role and experiences would be no different. Depression isn't less important or easier to cope with than other illnesses because it is a mental condition rather than a physical one. In fact it is often more difficult to cope with, both because of the stigma associated with depression, and because the depressed person may themselves be in denial about their condition.

Just remember: what you are doing counts. It counts a lot; especially to the person you are helping.

So if any of the feelings described at the beginning of this chapter sound familiar, you can begin to see why. What you are experiencing is very common for any person who finds themselves in the caregiver's role.

I know that the road you are travelling is not an easy one. However, the good news is that there is a large – and ever-growing – body of knowledge that you can tap into to help you.

'Help?' you ask.

Yes, *help*.

When caregivers were asked what advice they could offer to fellow caregivers, one of the things they said was most important was to admit that you need help and not to waste one more minute before seeking appropriate resources. And these resources are out there.

Tapping into the available knowledge and finding resources to support you will help you care for your depressed loved one as they travel their own road to recovery. And most importantly, this will help you carry out your role as a caregiver without losing yourself in the process.

The caregiver's role

Caregivers are playing an increasingly important role in caring for people with a variety of acute and chronic conditions, including depression. In the US, the use of the word 'caregiver' in newspapers and other media tripled between 1990–4 and 1996–2001.[1] It is an acknowledged and valuable role that we now know quite a bit more about, because of the huge social and economic contribution they are now making.

Around 2.3 million Australians are providing care for family members or friends with a disability, mental illness, chronic condition or those who are frail or aged. This represents one in every five households, although it's thought that this figure is an underestimate because many don't declare the role they are playing out of loyalty to their loved one. Conservative estimates show that carers save the Australian economy $16 billion annually.

Types of caregiving are usually divided into two categories: formal and informal. Formal caregivers are usually medical or mental health professionals (doctors, nurses, health aides or therapists) and the majority of formal caregiving takes place in a supervised medical setting – for example, a hospital or institution.

Informal caregiving is just that – informal. It is unpaid care provided by family, friends and community, based on their relationship with the person who is ill and their desire to help that person. It is not given in a formal setting and generally speaking is not supervised. The demand for caregivers is growing as hospital stays get shorter and the incidence of depression increases, and this means that more and more caregiving responsibility is falling to informal caregivers.

Levels of caregiving depend on the number and intensity of the care requirements. Caregiving may range from occasional support to scheduled (and unscheduled) visits of a defined frequency to full-time, round-the-clock care. Most often, you would see occasional support and regular visits provided by informal caregivers. While informal caregivers do provide full-time care, if the affected person requires this level of caregiving, it is most likely advisable to seek professional help.

Most people who find themselves being an informal carer assume the role with little or no training or guidance. Typically, they are unaware of what specific support may be available to help them with the caregiving role. And most people don't have a plan with respect to their caregiving commitment. Informal caregivers often find themselves in the position of learning and planning as they go, which is a bit like trying to fix a flat tyre on your car while it is travelling down the road at a fast rate (not the easiest thing in the world!).

The informal caregiver network of family and friends are often the people who play the most important role of all in helping a depressed loved one recover. Family and friends may in fact notice the signs of depression before the affected loved one is aware of what is happening themselves.

This informal network is often instrumental in encouraging the depressed loved one to seek help in the first place, to get diagnosed and receive the appropriate treatment. These carers provide unconditional love and support with extraordinary compassion and patience. Many people recovering from depression credit their network of caregivers with literally 'saving their lives'. In fact, in research completed for *Back from the Brink*, the support of family and friends was rated second only to exercise as the most effective aid in overcoming/managing depression.

What to expect as a caregiver

Doctors Laura Epstein Rosen and Xavier Francisco Amador addressed typical issues that caregivers of depressed loved ones may experience in their book, *When Someone You Love is Depressed – How to Help Your Loved One Without Losing Yourself*.[2] They found that most caregivers are so focused on helping their loved one that they don't realise the extent to which their loved one's depression is affecting them.

Dr Rosen and Dr Amador found that relatives of depressed people 'suffer from increased worry, resentment, and exhaustion'. They also found that if you are married to a person suffering from depression, the probability that you will undergo divorce is about nine times higher than for couples where depression is not a factor.

Feeling sad and depressed

Depending on your individual experience, you may or may not be surprised to learn that one of the biggest issues carers face is becoming depressed themselves. Research on interactions between depressed persons and strangers found that people in contact with depressed persons for even a short period of time reported feeling 'down' themselves. Depression is not contagious per se, but it is striking that those in the study commented on the depressed peoples' 'negative attitude' or 'lack of energy'.

Feeling anxious

Caregivers of depressed persons also talk about feeling as if they are walking on eggshells when they interact with the depressed person in their life. They are hyper-vigilant not to say or do anything that they believe could make their loved one's depression worse. They report feeling anxious, a normal result of constantly feeling that you are 'on guard'. The problem with being 'on guard' all the time, aside from the anxiety you might experience, is that you might also miss the opportunity for meaningful – and healing – discussions with your depressed loved one about how you and they are feeling.

Feeling lonely or isolated

When the strangers in Dr Rosen and Dr Amador's study were asked how being around the depressed person affected them, one thing they said was that they would not be willing to spend time with the depressed person in the future.

Clearly if you are in the role of carer, you have committed to spending time with the depressed person. But what about everyone else? If people tend to withdraw from those affected by depression, chances are the caregiver may also find themselves negatively impacted by a shrinking circle of friends and less attentive family members. This is compounded by the fact that your depressed loved one may not be 'the person they used to be' and you may be experiencing profound longing for the relationship you used to have.

Feeling frustrated or angry

Caregiving can be demanding and stressful. It is not unusual for caregivers to report feeling angry that their depressed loved one doesn't seem to be getting better or is withdrawn or hostile towards them. This can be especially true if the depressed loved one has attempted suicide. Anger is a normal response to this situation; however you may feel that the last thing you want to do is express how you are feeling to your depressed loved one when you are angry. It may feel as if your loved one is suffering enough and talking about your own feelings will make matters worse.

Dealing with angry feelings in any relationship can be tricky. Working through this with a depressed loved one is even more complicated. However it is important to the depressed loved one and caregiver alike to be able to constructively deal with these types of feelings.

Feeling guilty

We tend to be our own worst critics. This seems to be especially true for carers, who often hold themselves to an impossible standard of perfection. This of course leads to guilt. It can become a vicious cycle: you feel angry over something that your depressed loved one has done or said, and then you feel guilty because you felt angry. Or you are sad and guilty because you ask yourself 'How can I selfishly afford to feel sad when my loved one is so depressed?'

Once you are in this vicious cycle, it is a battle that you cannot win. Not only that, but it takes you away from what you are trying to do – help your depressed loved one.

In their own words

A Beyondblue report, 'The Experience of Caring for a Person with Depression', gathered the following responses from carers about their experiences of caring for loved ones with depression.[3]

> *The implications for me? It just completely changed my whole life.*
>
> *I just couldn't see my life. I was thinking, I don't want to be his nursemaid ... I want to have a life, and I want to enjoy it.*
>
> *My mobile's by my bed at night. It's on right now. So [it feels like my life is] revolving around her.*
>
> *The only time you have any peace is when they are in hospital. That's the only time. And I know it sounds dreadful but when the doctor says 'I'm going to put her in', it feels like there is a weight taken off my shoulders. And when he says 'I'm going to keep her in for another week', I say to myself, phew, another week, wonderful.*
>
> *There's this awful grief that goes on. It's not like when someone dies, the grief is there for a year or so and then it is finished. But our grief goes on and on. And you think this time it will be all right. Then you fall in a hole again. The grief is continual and that is what wears me down.*
>
> *Of course, as a parent you have hopes and dreams that they will go to school, uni – now I just want her to be alive. You have to let go of your expectations and dreams for them.*
>
> *Your energy levels are so depleted ... it's depressing, actually.*
>
> *You have to find other ways to get your life back because otherwise if you're waiting [for them to get better], you could be waiting a very, very long time. Maybe forever.*
>
> *I love him, but at times I think I hate him.*
>
> *The impact on my family? I think it's been pretty devastating.*

She completely cut me off. So I lost total contact with my sister for three or four years.

One of my sisters-in-law still thinks it is contagious and doesn't want my sister in the house. There is a lot of fear in … families about this.

She was of the opinion that he should just snap out of it and go out and get a job and pull his socks up and that sort of thing. And as a result the marriage did break up.

When my son became unwell, they just sort of drifted off, there was no contact.

I have lost one of my best friends who said we don't invite you [out] anymore because you're no fun to be with. And that really hurts … But some do [understand] and are good. So it's half and half.

… the lack of family has made it worse because there is no one else who can step in and look after her or be there with her. It always comes down to me.

The silver lining

Doing good for others makes us healthier. This conventional wisdom can be found in every religion and spiritual practice on the planet. Scientific research is now starting to shed light on the physical reasons for this. 'Helper's high' appears to stimulate the release of feel-good brain chemicals, just as runners experience with 'runner's high', where the brain releases a rush of endorphins after strenuous exercise.

It goes without saying that if you are caregiver, you occupy a very special niche in this world. You might not have thought that caregiving would have benefits for you as well as the person you are caring for. The challenge is to balance these benefits with the aspects of caregiving that can sap our physical, emotional, mental and spiritual wellbeing if we are not mindful.

Tools for caregivers

One theme comes through loud and clear in all of the medical, mental health and anecdotal information about the caregiver's role. The first thing a caregiver needs to do is realise that they will need help. Try answering the questions in the self-assessment below to see how you're faring.

A SELF-ASSESSMENT FOR CAREGIVERS
During the past week, have you:

- Found yourself trying to 'do it all' and resisting asking for help from others?

- Had problems falling asleep, or staying asleep?

- Had back pain, headaches, or otherwise felt ill?

- Had trouble keeping your mind on the task at hand?

- Experienced low energy or exhaustion?

- Felt completely overwhelmed?

- Felt frustrated over something you can't change?

- Experienced emotional outbursts such as crying spells, depression, anger, guilt, loneliness or anxiety?

- Felt that no one understands?

- Felt a loss of personal time or privacy?

If you answered 'yes' to any of these questions, you are likely to be experiencing caregiver stress. It's extremely important to look after your own wellbeing. Your next step should be to see your GP or find yourself a support group.

This self-assessment tool is based on self-assessment tests from the American Medical Association and the Oregon Department of Human Services.[4]

Remember the flight safety briefing about oxygen masks?

In the event of a loss of cabin pressure an oxygen mask will drop down over your head. Place it over your nose and mouth as the flight attendants are demonstrating. If you are seated next to a small child, please put on your mask first before helping the child.

While it might seem a bit counterintuitive, in order to help anyone else you really do have to take care of yourself first.

Nerida and Brian's Story

Carer: Nerida Egan; Caree: Brian Egan

Brian Egan is from outback Queensland and lost everything in the drought. A veteran and farmer, Brian suffered from Post Traumatic Stress Disorder and depression. He tried many different medications and went to see several psychiatrists but nothing seemed to work. At one point, so depressed he couldn't even talk, a psychologist suggested he get involved with a charity. That was when Brian started voluntary work and remembered the importance of community spirit. He set up Aussie Helpers in the hope of helping farmers in need. He certainly has done just that, with Aussie Helpers continuing to grow in outback Australia, allowing Brian to reach more farming families in desperate situations.

Sydney broadcaster Alan Jones has referred to Brian as the 'Mother Teresa of the outback'. Brian's dramatic recovery is a testament to his belief in Mother Teresa's philosophy that 'giving is receiving'. He was nominated for Senior Australian of the Year in 2008.

Nerida's story

Brian and I have been married for 35 years. I was attracted to him because he was handsome and just … you know, a nice guy. He was a quiet man, not very open with his feelings, but maybe that was what attracted me to him. Even 35 years ago his moods were unusual, he used to go into this really quiet time. I just thought he was different from other people.

It wasn't until 10 years into the marriage that I realised something was really wrong. We were living in Dalby at the time and Brian was working in Toowoomba. Someone knocked on my door late one night and told me that Brian was in intensive care in Dalby Hospital. Naturally I raced down there and they thought he'd had a heart attack or … well, they weren't really sure.

It took five years of going to doctors and specialists and that sort of thing until they'd decided it was a panic attack. He'd collapsed at the wheel of the car driving home from Toowoomba. In those five years he took up heavy drinking because he didn't seem to be coping with life.

His moods were probably the hardest thing to deal with because we had four small children. He'd be in a good mood one minute, and the next minute he'd be very quiet, or he'd be grumpy. It was hard. The children would come home and I'd think 'I'd better keep him quiet' or warn the children 'Dad's in one of his moods. Don't go near him'. Our eldest daughter told me that she grew up frightened of her father. He never bashed them or hit them or anything, it was just 'Go away and leave me alone'. He loved the girls but it was just … whatever was going on inside his head.

One day he walked in and our second eldest was probably only six and she was sitting on the floor and he went to kick her and I said 'Look, either you go and do something or I'm off', because I wouldn't put up with that. So he packed a bag and went down and saw his psychiatrist and said 'You've got to put me in somewhere' so they put him in the psychiatric unit in Brisbane.

He was in there for quite some weeks. He came home and … I can't say he was cured, but he seemed to be a little bit better for a while. And then the drinking started and it was my fault … it was always somebody else's fault.

He wasn't sleeping which made it difficult for me because I couldn't get any sleep either. Brian suffered from sleep apnoea but we didn't know that at the time either. He'd stop breathing and I'd think 'Oh, Lord, don't let him start again' because he was that horrible. And then all of a sudden I'd have this guilt trip and I'd give him a bit of a nudge in the ribs. He was just … the moods. There was no affection, nothing. He was as cold as a lump of wood.

We ended up moving to the country and bought the farm. He was working away and rang me and said 'I'm sick' and I said 'well you

better come home'. So he drove home and he'd just sit and sit and sit, wouldn't do anything, had no life. He wouldn't speak and if he did speak it was only to criticise something.

I rang the doctor one day and I don't even know why. I said to the doctor 'Look, there's something happening and I can't put up with this', so we went in there and this doctor said he was suffering with depression. Then he started seeing a government psychologist and seemed to be going good, he liked her. But every few weeks they'd change them and eventually he said 'I'm not going back there because you go, you just get to know them, then you go again and there's a new one and you sit down and they say, 'Well, tell me what your problem is', and I have to go through it over and over again'.

So that wasn't working, and we went back to his doctor and I think his doctor may have said something like 'Were you in one of the services?' Something clicked and then Veteran's Affairs came into the picture and he got a referral to go and see Dr John Gibson and John, being experienced, picked up on the depression and put him in hospital.

He spent 12 months in there and I was managing the family and everything by myself. They were hard times. I mean there were times where we were flat out putting bread on the table. But I never bothered Brian with any of that because he had enough to cope with, I felt.

Greenslopes [Brian's hospital] actually had a course, there were five of us ladies invited down there to learn how cope with people that were suffering from depression. When we went in there, us ladies were all in the same boat and I have to say we had a wonderful bitching session (laughs).

I used to patronise Brian because I didn't like the arguments and being blamed for everything so I'd just shut my mouth. But by patronising him, I didn't realise I wasn't helping him, and I was probably making things worse for myself because I was bottling everything up. I was lying in bed of a night not letting anyone know my heart was being ripped out.

So from then on I said how I felt. It still took time before I could have friends over, because if someone would come over, Brian would just go and hide. He wouldn't face people. And I couldn't go out to my friends because he didn't like being left alone and I have to say there were times when I was afraid to leave him alone.

I felt that I was becoming depressed. So I just stood up and said, 'Right, this is what I'm doing, you can come or you can stay' … so I just didn't give in to him anymore. Standing up to him and saying 'Right, I'm a big girl, and I'm your wife, but I've got a life too. I feed you, I keep you clothed, I'm here if you need me, but I've got to be able to breathe', definitely jolted him and gave him some accountability. He was making me feel worthless. I felt so useless because here was the man I loved and I couldn't do anything for him.

It's frustrating. There's times where you think 'Wake up, get over it. You know, I've got to put up with these things too. How selfish are you?' It's extremely hard on the partner. You know we feel for you, we love you, whether you're suffering with depression or not, we love you, but we're only human. I couldn't get him motivated to do anything, which was frustrating. I'd have to do everything plus look after the kids. It was so frustrating that he didn't care about how I felt. Maybe that sounds selfish, I don't know … but you know, I wanted him to understand how I felt.

The best advice I can give to wives in the situation I was once in is to not forget about yourself. You're very important. You must still have a life. You've got to have space, and your friends. Don't put him first because life goes on and you've got to keep your own sanity, and sometimes you question that too when you're living with someone with depression, because you think it's something you're doing that's not helping or you're doing the wrong thing. You question yourself all the time.

I left Brian on a number of occasions. But he had no one. If we hadn't gone back, I should imagine he would have done away with himself then and there, and that was what I was afraid of. And I thought, I don't hate the guy, I hate what he is, but I don't hate him.

There's been a dramatic turn-around from how he was back then to how he is today. Once he started Aussie Helpers, I could see change every day. It wasn't about him anymore. I mean, he still has hard days, but now he gets up and if he's feeling bad, he must think to himself, 'Well I haven't got time to think about this. Mrs so-and-so or Mr so-and-so needs a load of hay or they've got no food on the table to feed their kids, I've got to do this', so he focuses on doing for others instead of dwelling on his own problems.

We're so busy with Aussie Helpers, and there's days when I wake up and I say 'I don't want to play this game anymore' because, you know, you get tired. But once I'm there, and you get to talk to the people, I'm fine. It's very rewarding.

Brian has never been one to have many friends, but I know that there are a lot of people that respect him and I think that is good for him. I think he sees the sad things that are going on out there and thinks 'I thought I had it tough'.

Aussie Helpers has been his lifesaver. He'd be dead now if it wasn't for Aussie Helpers. The people in the bush have saved Brian's life. So if you can try to get your husband motivated into doing something for someone else, that can be really helpful. And [my other piece of advice is to] just love them. Because in the end, they'll love you back. It just takes a long time, and if you care enough about somebody, you'll hang in there.

Remembering it all is very hard for me actually because there's times there you sort of want to forget, but it's in the past now and I've got this husband that gives me cuddles now, doesn't just stand there like a light pole.

Carer's Tips: *Make sure you take care of yourself and don't forget about your own life – you're no good to anyone if you don't. Make time to regularly see and speak to your friends – you can't do this all by yourself.*

The Seven
Biggest
Frustrations
of Caregivers

The Seven Biggest Frustrations of Caregivers

WE CAN'T ALWAYS choose what comes into our lives, but we do get to choose how we react. We are all unique in that choice. However, when I talk to those who care for depressed people, I hear so many shared experiences that I thought it would be useful to share these common themes.

Every time I held a talk and/or book signing for my first book, *Back from the Brink*, several carers would come up to me and express their frustration and anxiety about not knowing how best to support a loved one with depression. I understand their situation well: I know that my parents, who supported me superbly during my prolonged depression, were often at a loss to know what to do themselves.

This chapter is organised around the seven things that in my experience are the biggest issues for caregivers:

1. Frustration

2. Rejection and isolation

3. Finding support

4. Feeling invisible

5. Side-effects of medication

6. Changes in the depressed person, and

7. Your own needs (and the children).

Some of these themes may resonate with you, others not so much so. When interviewing for this book, we asked people to rate the problems and frustrations they had in supporting their loved one with depression.

Their answers were:

Agree/Strongly Agree

I feel like I am being pushed away	76%
Depression has a negative impact on our sex life (if you are a partner)	61%
I feel like I don't know them anymore	60%
I can't find good resources to help me	53%
I wish they would just snap out of it	51%
I can't talk with anyone about the situation	42%
Health providers act like I don't exist	37%

FRUSTRATION

> *I tried to be so positive with him, encouraging him all the time, but I just couldn't seem to make things any better. I felt as if I had failed … why won't he bounce back?*
>
> *I know it's an illness but I couldn't help thinking, nothing's changed from six months ago. We have a nice house, two lovely kids, good family and friends … there's no reason to be depressed.*

In the not-too-distant past, people with mental illness or those who were psychologically vulnerable were often jailed or, in the best-case scenario, institutionalised. As Graham Thornicroft explains in his book *Shunned*, those who remained free of the system existed on the margins of society and experienced 'conflict within families, paternalism in treatment settings, lack of empathy at work, and bias in all manner of civil and social life'.[4]

Today, things have greatly improved, and there are a variety of treatments for those with mental illnesses. Knowledge that used to be restricted to those in the medical or psychiatric fields is fairly readily available to the average person; and, in turn, mental illness is far less stigmatised. We are now able to make use of the available information and educate ourselves, and we are encouraged to do so. Moreover, most people understand that depression is an illness. They know that depression has a variety of causes and most importantly, that it is treatable.

This understanding and knowledge gives caregivers great tools to help them support their depressed loved ones. Unfortunately, understanding and knowledge alone do not give carers immunity from frustration. It is also helpful to remember that understanding and knowledge don't change the nature of depression or the course of this illness.

Depression tends to be a chronic condition – it can last for a long time. There is not always a direct cause and effect between treatment and being able to see an improvement in your loved one's condition. It is easy to see why a carer may find him or herself thinking, 'Why can't they just snap out it?'

Please don't judge yourself if you sometimes feel this way. Feelings are not bad or good. They are just feelings; it's natural to have them. Try to acknowledge them as such.

Common sense tells us to take action on our feelings. That is not a bad idea, but your approach is going to depend on where you are in your story.

If your loved one has not been diagnosed and is not yet receiving treatment, your best course of action might be to see if you can encourage them to get help.

If your loved one is currently in treatment, your best course of action might be to do something that you'll find uplifting, something that will help you shake off your frustration. Get out of your environment and take a walk. Maybe reflect on elements of recovery that you have observed or that your loved one or their doctor has shared with you. Remember that everything counts. Sometimes just holding a feeling of gratitude for what you have – that your loved one is still in your life and did not suicide, that you have the resources to seek and receive help, that you have a source of support (even just one person is okay) – is enough to shift your frustration and allow you a sense of peace.

Let a little light in.

Rejection and isolation

> *He became non-communicative, withdrawn, he just stopped talking to me.*
>
> *She didn't want to go out, so we didn't go out. We knocked back invitations, they stopped coming, so we stayed home.*
>
> *When I meet people I can't really present what is going on in my life. It's more that [my depressed loved one is] private and doesn't like me to discuss their private details with other people. But the trouble is my private details are so interlinked with theirs that I almost feel I don't have a story of my own.*

If you read the statistics on how many people have suffered from or are suffering from depression in our country, it's staggering. According to Beyondblue, the national depression initiative, one in five Australians will suffer from depression during their lifetime. In any given year, one million adults and 100,000 young people struggle with depression. Even more sobering is the knowledge that at least two loved ones support every person with depression – that's another two million people affected by depression. And that's just in Australia. But the fact is that depression is a global issue. There is not a person walking on the planet who is immune to the effects of depression.

The good news? You are not alone.

It is not unusual for us to understand and accept information without having it change how we feel. For example, you probably already know that depression is a serious health issue that affects many people. But on a heart level, how do you feel? What does this mean for you and your depressed friend or family member? Do your feelings change even though the statistics speak for themselves?

Probably not.

Many caregivers still find themselves feeling alone and lonely; knowing that others are in the same situation doesn't necessarily help. They are also likely to feel pushed away as they attempt to help their depressed loved one. In fact carers often find themselves struggling with feelings of rejection and isolation at the same time as they are trying to help a loved one who is struggling with depression.

If you have never experienced depression, it can be difficult – if not impossible – to imagine what being depressed is like. I have heard depression described as being like finding yourself locked up in a tiny, windowless room. All aspects of life feel as if they have been compressed. The depressed person can't see out and others can't see in. Everyone loses a little perspective.

Depressed people may not be aware of the effect they are having on those around them. At the same time they may be hypersensitive without knowing why. If they do have any insight into their depression and how it affects those around them, their reaction may very well be to retreat out of shame instead of reaching out for comfort. They may feel annoyed that depression has robbed them of the things they used to find interesting and enjoyable, and might respond by lashing out at those closest to them.

Let's try looking at these feelings of isolation and rejection in a different context. If your loved one were taken away from you for some period of time – say he or she was sent to a remote location for a work assignment – it would be natural for you to feel lonely during the course of their absence. You might even feel rejected because they agreed to the assignment in the first place.

Depression is like someone has been taken away. If you have a friend or family member who is depressed, feeling rejected or isolated is a normal reaction to the circumstances you are actually dealing with as a caregiver.

It may be small comfort, but truly, you are not alone. It is important to continue to reinforce this fact until you not only know it, but you can feel it in your heart as well. This is one reason that finding a support group or reaching out to your network of family or friends is so important. Celebrate and share your health. Take the steps you need to look after yourself and stay healthy. Look forward to the time that your depressed loved one can join you in that celebration. Keep saying to yourself, 'This too will pass'.

Finding support

> *The average person doesn't have a clue [where to go to for help]. You rely on your doctor.*
>
> *I had no experience, no background. I didn't know who to turn to. You don't want to tell your friends so I just didn't know who to turn to.*
>
> *GPs just don't know what's available.*

We live in interesting times. Technology has made it possible for us to have non-stop access to every type of media known to man. Living in an industrialised society with good access to education has given people across all walks of life the opportunity to have a decent livelihood and to be financially independent. And we also have greater mobility than at any point in the history of civilisation. We also have the cost of this mobility, which is a decreased sense of community.

The overabundance of information, the shrinking sense of tangible community and our attachment to being independent can be challenges when we are the caregiver of a depressed person and not sure where to turn.

First, we need to accept that we need help.

Then, we need to find it.

The good news is that there are many quality resources available. A comprehensive list of organisations providing support for carers and their loved ones is contained in the Resources section on page 217.

Feeling invisible

> *The hoops we had to go through to get her in to see [the professional] that we wanted were ridiculous.*
>
> *Not cooperating with parents or carers is absolutely standard.*
>
> *For God's sake, why can't health professionals consult the carer, too? I know there are privacy problems and that sort of thing, well too bad. You're going to have to sort it out because the professionals are running on about one-tenth of the information they need.*

There are two sides to every story. Here's one that may sound familiar to you. Caregivers of depressed loved ones often complain that doctors and psychologists act as if they don't exist. On the other hand, doctors and psychologists often complain about caregivers getting in the way of treatment and even taking their anger and frustration out on the health care providers.

Clearly, both sides stand to gain by improving communication. At least that is the suggestion of the US National Family Caregivers Association (NFCA). They cite 'better care for the patient, less stress and illness for the caregiver, more efficient use of doctors' time, reduced costs for the health care system, and more satisfaction for all concerned' as compelling reasons why both caregivers and health care providers might want to take an active interest in making sure that they communicate effectively. Here are the tips that the NFCA recommends based on input from both caregivers and health care providers.

Advice from the health care provider to the caregiver:

- Write questions down so you won't forget them. Health care providers, especially doctors, are usually on tight schedules. Try not to ramble. If you have a lot to talk about, consider making a consultation appointment.

- Educate yourself about depression. This is one instance when living in the information age is very useful. With all the information on the internet it is easier than ever before.

- Learn the routine at your doctor's office and/or the hospital so you can make the system work for you, not against you.

- Recognise that while health care providers are highly trained, not all questions have answers – especially those beginning with 'why'.

- Remember that you and the health care provider are on the same side – you both want to help. Be careful to separate your anger or frustration about the situation from your feelings about the health care provider.

- Appreciate what the health care provider is doing to help and say thank you from time to time.[5]

Side-effects of medication

> *Our love life used to be very good. She used to enjoy making love, she used to have orgasms … on medication it's all gone. She feels nothing … so we don't make love.*
>
> *We haven't had sex for two years. At first I didn't know he had depression – I thought he didn't love me.*

There is no question that drug therapy is a key component in treating depression. However, like any medication, antidepressants may have side-effects. These may only last for a few weeks and subside with no further intervention, or they might persist during the course of treatment. Side-effects of drugs are the biggest reason why people stop taking their medication. However, stopping a prescribed antidepressant can trigger unpleasant withdrawal symptoms; also, if the patient stops taking what has been prescribed for them, it can delay their recovery.[6]

Patients may also be tempted to reduce the dose they were prescribed in order to lessen the impact of side-effects. While it may be entirely possible to reduce side-effects by reducing or changing the dosage, this should always be done with the prescribing health care provider's advice – not by the patient (or caregiver) alone.

What does this mean for you as a caregiver? It means that in addition to dealing with the symptoms of your loved one's depression, you may find yourself also dealing with the side-effects of the medication used to treat it.

It is important to know what medication your depressed friend or family member has been prescribed and what side-effects might be associated with these drugs. Bear in mind that it is not uncommon for more than one drug to be prescribed. For example, many people suffering from depression also suffer from anxiety. The goal of prescribing drugs in combination is to alleviate as many of the symptoms as possible and help the depressed patient recover as quickly as possible.

What about alternative medicine?

Alternative medicine approaches in conjunction with Western medicine are often quite effective. However, you must not extend this philosophy to the drug regimen that your depressed loved one has been prescribed to treat their illness.

Herbal remedies are drugs: many of our modern pharmaceuticals were derived from herbs and other plants. The active ingredients in antidepressants or anti-anxiety medication can interact with herbal medicines in unpredictable ways.

If your depressed loved one wants to try a natural remedy, make sure that they talk to their doctor first.

It is very important that your depressed loved one does not make decisions about medication without consulting a doctor. It is not unusual when people start feeling better for them to decide to taper off their medication. It takes time to address the chemical changes that may have occurred in the brain as a result of depression. This means that even if the depressed person is feeling better, it is important for them to continue taking their medication until their doctor says that it is okay to stop. Stopping is a gradual process and must be done under a doctor's supervision.

Sometimes a depressed person may feel that they should take more medication than they were prescribed if they are not seeing the results they expect or want. Again, changes in dosage must be discussed with a doctor.

One of the most complained-about side-effects of antidepressants is sexual dysfunction. This can include loss of libido, difficulty in achieving an erection, or in reaching orgasm. For the spouse or partner caregiver it may seem like one more aspect of the relationship that depression has taken away.

Medication may also cause nausea, nervousness, insomnia, agitation or weight gain.

What can you do about these side-effects? First, reassure your loved one that this new round of depression-related challenges is not going to drive you away. Your loved one has taken an important step towards recovery in deciding to follow their health care provider's advice and include medication as part of their treatment. They may feel a bit dismayed and insecure that the medication that will help them recover from their depression has added a new layer of highly personal and potentially uncomfortable issues for them to deal with.

If they are experiencing side-effects, encourage them to talk to their health care provider about the possibility of changing medications, adjusting the dosage or even switching the time of day that the drug is taken. For example taking a drug early in the day can reduce the incidence of insomnia. Lifestyle changes can help as well. Reserving the bedroom for sleeping or lovemaking – rather than for watching television, for example – can also help with insomnia or sexual dysfunction. Taking a walk together or getting regular exercise can help with weight gain, as can a change in diet to healthier fare if that is warranted.

Above all, remember that healing is a process. Try to cultivate patience.

Changes in the depressed person

> *You grieve for the person they were or who they could have been.*
> *This is not the person I married four years ago.*

According to William Styron, author of *Darkness Visible*, '(the word) "depression" is not a good description of what depressed people feel'. People suffering from depression can exhibit a variety of symptoms ranging from sadness to anxiety disorders to agitation.

Most depressed persons report that they lose interest in things that they used to like and find that the joy they once experienced in their day-to-day lives is gone. They feel sad and hopeless and may be prone to bouts of crying. But depressed people also report feeling irritable and restless. They may have trouble concentrating and feel like they are not as smart as they used to be. Changes in sleep patterns are not unusual, nor are changes in weight. Depression also seems to be associated with a feeling of fatigue and physical heaviness: walking from point A to point B seems to take inordinate effort.

The most confident person may find themselves doubting their abilities and find that their self-esteem has faded to almost nothing. Outgoing people may suddenly become introverted and withdrawn. People who are normally optimistic may begin to adopt a negative view of everything around them. They may talk about how there is no future for them and might have thoughts of, or talk about, suicide.

For the depressed person, depression is a complex illness that may have many symptoms. For the caregiver, though, there is a common thread.

The family member or friend that you hung out with, worked with, were raised by or fell in love with is no longer the person you thought you knew. This is a huge shock for most caregivers.

Carers may be hesitant to admit that there is a sense of grief associated with this realisation. After all, your loved one has not died. They are just depressed. But this grief or sense of loss is very real. It stems from the fact that the person you know and love is, in a way, gone. They are not the same: depression changes people and there is no getting around that. And so this sense of loss or grief, while uncomfortable, is quite normal.

If you find yourself wondering 'who is this person?' as you provide care for your depressed loved one, check in with your feelings and see if you are indeed experiencing some grief. If the answer is 'yes', don't panic: there are many wonderful resources to help people process grief. Perhaps you might be willing to explore this for yourself. A good psychologist and many of the carer organisations listed in the Resources section on page 215 will be able to suggest strategies that could help with this.

No one can guarantee that your loved one will be exactly the same as they were before they became depressed. This does not mean that your relationship is over. It probably does mean that it will change. Again, please don't view the word 'change' as meaning for the worse. It might be a change for the better; only time will tell. I know this is one of the most difficult realities you will face as a caregiver.

Your own needs (and the children)

I did go through a period of being resentful that I wasn't able to have problems, or if I had them, they had to be sorted out away from home.

He hasn't worked since last August. I've had to re-finance our home. I care for the animals, I'm the one working 10-hour days at work, and yet everyone's going 'poor Tom has got depression, poor Tom', like he's an alcoholic. It's like – poor me! I don't have a sex life, I'm running everything myself, when can I have care? And you do get very resentful.

I don't know whether it was because [some family members] thought they were going to catch it [it was in the genes] or something. But they … would back off and you wouldn't hear from them. And it hurt. I was really hurt.

Both my children have been scared that he was going to hurt me "

Many carers supporting a partner worry about how that person's depression is impacting on their children. This is not to be taken lightly as children are very perceptive and it is certainly something that should be closely monitored. What's more, it is very hard to find practical advice on how this concern should best be handled. For detailed information on this, see page 179.

Take care of yourself

There is a sombre irony here, in that carers of depressed loved ones are at greater risk than the general population of becoming depressed themselves. Caregivers, when surveyed, often report poorer health than those of a similar age and demographic who are not functioning in a caregiver role. The reason is that the caregiving role exposes you to a higher level of stress, greater demands and more fatigue and isolation than most people encounter in their daily lives. The amount of time that you spend caregiving, as well as the intensity of your role, may worsen the impact.

This is often compounded by carers reporting that some family and friends stop making contact. This is usually because of the stigma associated with depression, or not knowing what to say or do. Whatever the reason, the combination of the extra load due to caring for someone with depression and the withdrawal of emotional support from family and friends is devastating for carers.

There is no getting around the fact that being a caregiver takes a mental, physical and emotional toll on the individual providing care. Fortunately, we now know quite a bit about ways to mitigate this impact.

First, make sure that you remain open to getting help for yourself. Caregivers say that sometimes this is the hardest thing for them to do, and it can be harder for men than women. Remember that this is not the time for heroics. If it is hard for you to accept the idea of help, try thinking about this issue from your loved one's point of view. They will notice if your mental, physical or emotional health starts to decline. People who are depressed might not seem like their old selves but they do tend to be extraordinarily perceptive. They will feel guilty if they sense that you are suffering. You don't want your loved one to bear the burden of this guilt on top of dealing with their depression, do you? Of course not.

So please, take good care. Be gentle on yourself but take action. See the relevant chapters and the Resources section for details of organisations and support groups that may be of help.

'I think w
focused on a
nothing else

became so

isting Sarah,

eally existed.'

Sarah* and Richard's* story
*(*names have been changed)*

Carer: Richard; Caree: Sarah

Richard is a businessman and health professional who has substantial experience in the mental health area. Despite this background, he and his wife found it incredibly difficult when their daughter Sarah became depressed after being subjected to bullying at school and began cutting herself.

Richard's story

Sarah grew up as a very loving child in a happy family relationship. She was always relatively reserved, but put a lot of weight on personal relationships with her friends and her family. She grew up doing sport and doing quite well at it and really engaging in things that children of her age do. But there was always just a fairly reserved trait to her personality.

She enjoyed school in the early years, but it got a little problematical for her as she approached the senior end of junior school, so that's say Year 5 and 6. Probably in hindsight that's when some of the symptoms of her depression started to show, when there were some issues with other children. I guess for some kids that would have been seen as just a bit of schoolyard knock-about behaviour, but because of Sarah's own personality, she took those issues very much to heart. She didn't want to go to school. She believed that people didn't like her and there was no amount of rational discussion that could assist and relieve the things she was going through. As painful as it is, everybody goes through it at various times, but because of her personality, she took it very much to heart and was very affected by what she saw as rejection, and at times, outright nastiness.

As parents we obviously did our very best to support Sarah emotionally. We discussed it together and also went to see the school principal, who I must say was not particularly helpful. In the end we decided that Sarah would change schools. Sarah was actively involved in the choice of the school and that happened at the end of year 6.

The first year of high school started off fairly well. She struggled like most students do to make peer relationships in a new environment but she formed a couple of friendships that were very meaningful to her. Unfortunately, some of the bullying traits started to raise their head again, and I guess like in any situation she could not be seen as totally blameless. As she was growing up maybe she needed to ask herself if what she was doing was appropriate or inappropriate. Maybe she was seen as a soft target by some of the other children at school.

The bullying took the form of name calling and exclusion from activities that she wanted to be involved in. She wasn't a drinker or a substance user and because that was quite common at this particular school, she was excluded from some groups that she wanted to be involved in. A lot of it was fairly subtle. The isolated incidents don't mean a whole lot one by one but over a consistent period of time can weigh somebody down.

But over the next couple of years I must say there were some very good times for her as well as times when the bullying overpowered her. This led her to engage in some self-harming behaviour which was deeply alarming to us. Like most people who are confronted with someone else's self-harming behaviour, we found out about it by accident. Her brother saw some scratches on her legs which couldn't be explained by any rational reason, and then she revealed she was harming herself by cutting.

For many people feeling intense psychological pain, the self-harm actually releases some of their own psychological pain. We just asked her what the issues were, was something bothering her. We asked her firstly how these scratches on her leg occurred. She was unable to give an explanation and became quite distressed and angry that we asked her. When that period of time passed, she started to talk in more depth about some of the things that were happening to her.

Sarah was the sort of girl who puts on a happy face because that's what she feels she should do. She's always had a strong sense of spirit, of wanting to be okay, of wanting to be on top of issues in her life, but unfortunately like most people when they're worn down, those issues really got on top of her.

The cutting incidents happened on three or four separate occasions. We engaged with a psychologist in our local area who offered some help, but I thought was unduly intrusive on other areas of Sarah's life that she didn't wish to engage with. I don't think he engaged her on a meaningful level in the areas that needed discussion, so that series of counselling sessions was terminated. The counsellor at the time suggested Sarah was still a child at risk and if we removed her from the counselling situation she would be forced to report us to DoCs. My response to that was that's absolutely fine, please do what you have to do, but as a parent when you have a reasonable grip on these issues yourself, you can actually sense that this therapeutic relationship at this time was not beneficial to Sarah. Be it right or be it wrong, we made what we felt was an informed and caring decision for Sarah.

The psychologist had been recommended by the school. Unfortunately for Sarah the willingness to fully engage wasn't there because of her age. At 14 it might be difficult to accept that something might be wrong. And then to be different to your peer group, that you so desperately want to be part of, was hard to take.

During this time, Sarah was certainly off her game with the schoolwork and struggled to keep up. Once again in hindsight, I would have taken her to a psychiatrist for treatment for depression earlier. I actually believe that she was depressed and that the psychologist wasn't using Cognitive Behaviour Therapy (CBT) with her which would have been particularly useful. She was much more engaged in a psychoanalytic type model of what's making you cut yourself ... whereas I believed that Sarah really needed help on challenging unhelpful thoughts.

Once we stopped Sarah seeing the psychologist she did fairly well. She seemed a little more resilient; she certainly had an enormous amount of support from her mother and myself and also her grandmother. Really the roles of grandparents should never be underestimated. Sarah had a grandmother who was actively involved in her life. She was very interested in her welfare and development. Very often because the grandparent is once removed from the family home and there is a good relationship between the child and the grandparent, they may reveal things that are helpful. In Sarah's case, her grandmother gave her strong reassurance that things would be okay, that she would be OK.

In year 10 there was some more bullying that was more distressing for her and once again, the school didn't intervene as one would have hoped. This resulted in quite marked self-abuse, self-harm, cutting and at that point, my wife and I made the decision to take Sarah to a psychiatrist. Sarah was asking for help. This was a very frightening situation for her. She certainly wanted to die. She believed that she had no place in her friends' circle; she saw no light at the end of the tunnel.

We found an empathetic, delightful psychiatrist through my connections at work. The psychiatrist involved the family in the care, and certainly engaged Sarah extremely well. She was still reluctant to go because she thought 'if I've got to go to a psychiatrist there is something wrong with me'. She had a desperate desire to feel okay and not have something wrong with her. It's very difficult to get through that cloud of thinking.

The psychiatrist prescribed a very low dose of antidepressants and tried CBT. Because my wife and I were prepared to be diligent and care for Sarah at home, she was able to stay at home rather than be admitted to hospital as a suicide risk.

She'd been unwell a lot of year 11 and had the classic signs of irritability and poor concentration. Sarah's irritability made her fairly difficult for us all to live with. She wasn't eating as much as she normally would. Her social interaction caused problems for her.

As her own condition started to deteriorate her school peers started calling her things like 'psycho child' which caused her and us a lot of distress.

The psychiatrist recommended that she not go to school for a period of time because she needed the support and safety of her home. Her mother and I shared the caring at home for Sarah. Sarah also had a cat for some time and the role the cat played in her care could never be underestimated. He sensed that something wasn't quite right and he actually spent a lot of time just sitting with her. It was very helpful for her because she had always loved this animal and it gave unconditional love.

It was a road to Damascus in recognising how unwell Sarah was. One night I noticed that she inflicted some fresh cuts on herself. When I questioned her she asked me could I please give her directions on how to 'cut properly' so that she could kill herself as she felt I knew how she could do this properly. My response was 'I'm not going to tell you because you're going to get well'. I guess as a parent that was one of the tougher things that has ever happened to me.

My wife, whilst being an absolute tower of strength for Sarah, was absolutely distressed, so I never actually shared Sarah's question with her for a number of years. She was acutely aware of how unwell Sarah was and of her desire to die. I didn't want to unduly worry her as we already had strong vigilance around Sarah. It was one of the more sobering moments of life. Perhaps the most sobering moment of my life and I hoped I was doing the right thing.

We pushed on and gave each other a lot of support. My mother was very supportive but we didn't get any other help ourselves. This is contrary to what I always advise other people and I would do it differently if I had my time over again. I think we became so focused on assisting Sarah nothing else really existed. We tried to keep things relatively normal. We'd go out and have a meal or coffee together. We tried to provide some balance to: a) help Sarah start to recover and b) help us get through this situation because when you're outside of the house, you're trying to do normal things.

Things started to improve about six to eight weeks after Sarah went off school. She was then able to return to school – a new school, which was very supportive. The principal could not have been more concerned about Sarah's welfare and wellbeing if she had been one of his own children. The school created an environment that was both safe and welcoming for Sarah.

She left school at the end of year 11 which had been discussed a couple of months before. She got a job that she liked and whilst there were still ups and downs her emotional state was much more stable. One could say that she has recovered. She has found a place in the world that works for her. She has found a peer group that works for her, and she's developed. She's always had a good relationship with her mother and I, but I think that relationship has developed with a much more solid foundation. Hopefully we have all grown intellectually, emotionally, as a family unit and as people from this absolutely distressing situation.

In retrospect, while I took an assertive approach with her first school I would have taken a much stronger approach. When dealing with a school principal I was very aware of not wanting to create a situation where the child may be further ostracised by being perceived as having an unduly difficult parent. In hindsight, I wouldn't care if the school had perceived me as Attila the Hun if I could have helped circumvent some of these issues for Sarah.

With the psychologist too, once again, in hindsight, I would have talked to Sarah and encouraged her to have an in-depth psychiatric consult and then taken advice on the best way forward based on that consult. I still believe that looking after her at home was in her best interests. I say that with full knowledge that some people need to be in hospital for their own safety and wellbeing.

I have worked with many people that have depression or another mental illness. It's a whole different story when the person you loved unreservedly is living through it. You feel fairly impotent because you can offer advice, you can offer support, but as a parent, you can't make it go away. I think as a parent one of the things we always try to do for our children, when they're in pain, when they've hurt themselves, is to make that hurt go away. This is a pain that doesn't go away with a panacea of ice cream, some attention, or sharing a joke. It just doesn't go away like that.

In terms of advice for other parents caring for depressed or mentally unwell children, I would say firstly that your child has an illness and like any illness your child needs to seek — or to have sought on their behalf — some form of treatment, so you know exactly what the issue is. Cutting, whilst it is distressing, is a symptom of some other illness that is causing it. I know some parents get annoyed at their children for doing it. There's no point being annoyed, it's really a sign that something's wrong and that this person is crying out for help. I'd say take them to a GP for assessment and if that leads to a recommendation of an appointment with a psychiatrist, I would go down that path unreservedly. Secondly, I would always suggest that you don't look for blame. Blame to me is a wasted emotion. Something has occurred, you need to respond, you need to interact, you need to be helpful. Parents need to work in a cohesive unit and males particularly are good at putting their heads in the sand. Thankfully I wasn't because I've got a bit of experience in this area, but the male parent really needs to support strongly both their child and their partner in this situation. And you need to work to make the family unit even more cohesive than it would normally be.

I would also strongly recommend that people read about it. I think books like Back from the Brink and Back from the Brink Too, with the real stories of people are incredibly helpful. One of the issues that you feel is a sense of isolation and just reading other people's stories tends to break that down. You might read ten stories and one of them clicks that these strategies can help me.

It's also important to try to maintain some normality in your life. To do a few simple things like go out to a movie, to be together, to go and have dinner out. Nothing top end, because nobody really feels like it, but just go to a nice café, have something to eat.

I think the greatest gift that is most freely given is the love of the parent to the child because whilst they feel they're not going to make it, you know that they can and will and you focus your love on that. It's doing the best you can for as long as you can.

Sarah is now well. She has reached a level of recovery where her quality of life allows her to do the things that everybody of her age should be able to do. She may well get ill again in the future, who knows … the crystal ball is a bit dark on that issue, but she now has more strength in terms of knowing what to do.

"

Introducing the Seven Steps

Introducing the Seven Steps

As I HIGHLIGHTED earlier, I formally interviewed over 550 people to make sure this book is relevant: 300 living with depression, and 250 carers. I have also been the leader of a mental health support group called GROW for two years. Since the launch of *Back from the Brink* I have spoken informally to hundreds of other sufferers and their caregivers at seminars and book signings. I have personally known the deepest depression, which led to four suicide attempts. I now know the impact this had on my family.

From this I know that being a carer for a depressed friend or family member is one of the hardest things you can do. Depression is a complicated disease with a complex recovery process. There isn't a direct cause and effect – at least not one that has been discovered yet – and there is no single pill or injection or set number of therapy sessions that once taken (or completed), guarantee a cure. But one thing is for certain: people do get depressed and they do recover.

Why seven steps?

We have previously discussed the seven frustrations/problems of being a caregiver. My aim with the Seven Steps is to address the frustrations of both those living with depression and their carers.

My thinking has been to keep them as simple as possible, to help you understand what to do in these difficult circumstances. Ideally, for reasons I will explain, they should be approached sequentially, but there are exceptions. As you will see, the steps are compartmentalised – which enables you to easily refer back to the section that is relevant for you. Use a highlighter pen to flag the information that resonates with you.

The Seven Steps are:

1. Building knowledge

2. Learning to listen

3. Finding the right help

4. Providing the best support

5. Finding help for you

6. Taking care of you

7. Surviving a crisis

What if my loved one is in crisis?

If you suspect your loved one is in crisis and in danger of harming themselves, or someone else, ask them: 'If you had to rate yourself between 1 and 10, where 1 is actively suicidal and 10 is feeling normal, where would you rate yourself?'

If they answer 5 or below, go straight to Step 7. Do not pass GO. This is the time to be gently firm and assertive.

Step 1: Building knowledge

The greatest frustration for sufferers is a loved one telling them to 'snap out of it'. The greatest frustration for a caregiver is having a loved one in pain, and not knowing what to do about it. This is why we have asked the Black Dog Institute, one of the pre-eminent mood disorder research bodies in the world, to compile a description of exactly what depression is, what causes it, and what the best evidence-based treatments are. We have also included traditional mental health treatments as well as proven lifestyle habits that help.

Step 2: Learning to listen

Listening cuts both ways. Although the only thing you can control is your own behaviour and skills, how you ask questions and respond certainly influences how your loved one communicates.

Caregivers frequently feel shut out; listening is a very important skill, and listening to your depressed loved one is vital. There is however, a qualification. Many new carers think that their loved one knows what is wrong and what needs to be fixed. This is rarely the case. When I went through my five years of hell there was no reason that I could rationally identify as the reason. This was extremely frustrating for me and I know my carers also struggled with this. So although you need to listen with open ears, you also need to listen in an active way, questioning what you hear.

With some kinds of depression, an event has precipitated the onset of the depression. With other forms of depression, the feelings can seemingly come from nowhere. The very complexity of depression highlights why good communication is essential. Good communication can only happen when good listening happens, and as one of my interviewees succinctly said, 'Good listening is learning to ask better questions'.

Step 3: Finding the right help

This step finally helps you to start doing something. Carers often feel ill-informed and helpless; but Step 3 is where the 'rubber hits the road'.

If you believe those who have gone before you, experienced carers say that if they had their time over again they would get an accurate diagnosis from a competent mental health professional much earlier. To help your loved one receive this, it is imperative that you have read through Step 1 and that you have an accurate understanding of the symptoms and possible causes that you'll find in Step 2. This information helps you sort out the questions you can ask if you accompany your loved one to see their doctor. If your loved one doesn't want you to come with them, you can help them prepare crib notes for the visit, with a clear agenda to follow with the doctor.

Step 4: Providing the best support

This is the reassurance step. Those new to the caregiving role sometimes believe that if their loved one sees a competent mental health professional, they will witness a quick recovery. Sometimes this does happen, but unfortunately it is rarely a smooth or predictable ride. This step reinforces that you are on the right track and that in offering your love and support in finding the right help you are helping out in the very best way.

Step 5: Finding help for you

It might seem hard to believe, but there is actually quite a lot of information and support out there – although it is not necessarily easy to understand 'the system' and how to access it. In this section we outline the different options for support and help for you, the caregiver. The Resources section in the back contains contact details for the various organisations.

Step 6: Taking care of you

Eighty-one per cent of carers report that their mental and/or physical health has been adversely affected by caring for someone with depression.

When you start this journey it is like swimming underwater to reach the end of the pool. Everything is a bit blurry but you swim frantically to reach the goal – in this case, your loved one's recovery.

You're trying to look after a family and be productive at work as well as caring for and finding the right help for your loved one. You find yourself letting pleasurable activities like catching up with friends and getting regular exercise slip, because you just want your loved one to get better.

Still you hold your breath, struggling to get to the end. You push on to bursting point. Suddenly you discover that the end of the pool isn't where you thought it is and, worse, you can't even see where it is.

For God's sake (and your own), take a breath.

This step shows you what you must do to both sustain the care and to preserve your own wellbeing.

Step 7: Surviving a crisis

Hopefully you won't have to face a loved one harming themselves or someone else, but it is infinitely preferable to be prepared. This step provides practical advice to help your peace of mind. You have done a wonderful thing for your loved one by buying and reading this book. Be gentle on yourself. You are doing the best you can.

Step 1: Building Knowledge

Step 1: Building Knowledge

I would like them to know that you can't 'snap out of it' any more than you can 'snap out of' diabetes. I would like them to face up to it and not stick their heads in the sand. I would like them to know that their own ignorance about the illness is not an excuse for ignoring it in another, and that such an attitude can make the sick person's suffering much worse.

If you find yourself in the role of caregiver, the first step is to educate yourself about depression. Learning about depression will help you – and your depressed loved one – in several ways.

Diagnosis

Regardless of your relationship with the depressed person (partner, parent or friend), the key word here is relationship. Dr Rosen and Dr Amador in their book, *When Someone You Love is Depressed*, suggest that an 'early warning signal' for depression can be your 'feelings and reactions to trouble in the relationship'. Most of us are conflict-averse (no one likes trouble!) and so it is not uncommon for us to try and ignore our feelings or observations that something is not right and may have been amiss for a while.

There are a lot of resources available to help you and your loved one begin to assess whether or not depression is contributing to the issues you are experiencing. You can begin simply. In fact the US Preventive Services Task Force suggest just two simple questions that doctors could ask to help them screen patients for depression:[7]

1. During the past two weeks, have you felt down, depressed or hopeless?

2. During the past two weeks, have you felt little interest or pleasure in doing things?

If the patient gives positive responses to these two questions, doctors are encouraged to conduct a more complete interview for depression symptoms and to ask the patient if they have had thoughts of death or suicide.

The more you know about depression and its symptoms, the better guidance you may be able to provide to your friend or family member. While receiving a diagnosis of depression is not great news, diagnosis is the first step in any successful treatment and recovery process.

UNDERSTANDING

> *Depression is an illness just like heart disease or diabetes. It is important to understand the symptoms and disease progression so you can tell if your friend or family member is getting better. You also want to be able to tell if they are getting worse or approaching a crisis.*

Decision-Making.

Because of the complex nature of depression, recovery generally involves a fair amount of decision-making, often based on how the depressed person is reacting to the therapy, medication, alternative approach or a combination of all of these.

I can tell you from personal experience that being in a state of depression is not conducive to decision-making. A friend or family member who is knowledgeable about depression and who can act as a liaison with the health care delivery system is of tremendous value to both the diagnostic and recovery processes.

Knowledge is power – so be careful

Knowledge does give us a sense of power. But we also need to understand our limits. How can we best employ our new understanding to help our depressed friend or family member?

It can be a fine line for many carers. Although we completely understand that we are not doctors or psychologists, we may well encounter health care practitioners who seem to know less about depression than we do. This is a hotly-discussed issue these days for the health care profession, especially for general practitioners (GPs). These doctors are likely to be the ones who see the person most often and who ideally would be the gatekeepers, conducting an initial screening for symptoms of depression and then referring the person to a specialist if warranted.

The best thing to do if you encounter a doctor who doesn't give you confidence in their mental health knowledge is to find another. Make use of the many resources available online (and elsewhere) to find health care professionals who have experience in this field. There are many skilled health care resources who can help you and your depressed loved one.

You might be asking: how can I not overstep the boundaries but still contribute in a proactive, helpful way? I think the best way is to think of your contribution in terms of being a member of a team.

Let's talk briefly about teams in the context of medical (or psychological) practice.

Health care professionals operate under what is called a 'scope of practice'. Scope of practice depends on their role as a practitioner (their training and certification), their role within their organisation and certain governmental regulations that may apply. For example, if you ask the receptionist at your medical clinic what a lab test result means, he or she will refer you to your doctor. If you press the issue, he or she may tell you that they are not allowed to interpret lab test results, even if they know what the results mean – only the doctor can do this. This is scope of practice.

Scope of practice definitions change. In the old days, health care tended to be very hierarchical, with the doctor in unquestionable command. More recently, the health care industry borrowed something important from the airline industry.

The airline industry once had a similar scope of practice culture: the pilot of the aircraft was in charge and the co-pilot and navigator followed his orders (this was before there were female pilots). But an interesting safety discovery was made: there were fewer near-misses and crashes when the people in the cockpit operated as a team with everyone contributing rather than holding back because the pilot was supposed to be making all the decisions. You only have an incredibly short time to correct something going amiss during a flight, and it turned out that the split second the co-pilot or navigator might spend worrying that they would offend the pilot by speaking out of turn was not in anyone's best interest! The airline industry set about changing the culture and the result was a team approach.

Similarly, in health care, doctors now delegate more care responsibility to nurses, nurse-practitioners and other qualified health care personnel. Patients are happier and quality of care is improved or, at the very least, not diminished.

What this means for you the carer, is that you may find your loved one seeing a number of mental health professionals, for example a GP, a psychiatrist, a psychologist and, if they are in hospital, there will also be nurses, nursing unit managers, a hospital psychiatrist and a hospital psychologist, and so on. There can be different opinions between the many parties and this can be confusing for your loved one and you. If there are conflicting views on optimal care, you and your loved one are probably best off discussing this privately with the provider who knows your loved one the best and who you most trust.

One last word: if you are a doctor or psychologist by profession, it is still wise (as I'm sure you already know) to keep a healthy boundary between your professional life and your personal relationship as a caregiver.

Addressing the needs of all the family

> *Let family and friends know how much support is needed and how important it is not to make judgments or to use the depression as a weapon in an argument.*

We know that depression is a disease that affects not only the person suffering from depression, but everyone around them. This is especially true in families, and families will need to take special care to make sure that the needs of all members are addressed during the process of recovery. Doing this will actually help support the depressed family member – it is caregiving in every sense of the word.

Why is this important? Because friends and family members can be invaluable in both the diagnostic and treatment processes.

It isn't unusual for people suffering from depression not to recognise the symptoms. It is the people around them – friends and family – who tend to notice first. Friends and family members also have the benefit of history – they know the person and have observed them over some period of time. This information can be useful in diagnosing the type of depression the person may be suffering from and this in turn helps determine the course of treatment.

Psychologists know that the course of depression can be worsened by what is called 'expressed emotion': hostility, criticism and emotional over-involvement. Psychologist David Miklowitz, professor of psychology at the University of Colorado, reported that 'an atmosphere of high expressed emotion multiplies the chance of relapse two to three times'.

'Patients become hyperaroused,' explains Miklowitz. 'Imaging studies show that fear centers are activated in the brain when depression-susceptible people hear a family member criticising them.' Similarly, a researcher at Harvard Medical School, Nassir Ghaemi, discovered that this atmosphere of expressed emotions actually seemed to impair the benefit of prescribed medications.[8]

In their book, *When Someone You Love is Depressed*, Laura Epstein Rosen and Xavier Francisco Amador talk about the impacts on relationship that might occur when a friend or family member is depressed.

If you have a friend or family member who is depressed, according to Rosen and Amador, you are likely to be dealing with two types of role changes. First, your role in the relationship is likely to change as a result of your loved one's depression. For example if you are a child and you have a parent who is depressed, your mother or father may not be able to fully function as a parent. You may find yourself on your own a bit: this can be disorienting. Your parent who is not depressed may be pulling double duty and trying to act as both mother and father: that will be stressful for them. And depending on your age, you may find that there is actually some role reversal: you may find yourself parenting your mother or father. Adult peer relationship roles will change as well.

The second role change will be that of being in the caregiver role itself. Your carer role will be defined in large part by your relationship to the depressed loved one. In other words, if you are a child of a parent who is suffering from depression, your role – and the issues you will be faced with – will be different than if you are an adult and have a partner who is depressed.

Financial situations can change. If the primary wage earner in the family is not able to work due to their depression, spouses or children who are of age may need to seek work, or the family may require social assistance. If you are in business with someone who becomes depressed, you may have to take on increased responsibility in order to keep your business going. Financial issues can put a tremendous strain on a relationship.

Personal and social routines change when you have a depressed friend or family member. Activities that they previously enjoyed may not be of interest while they are depressed – this will affect you if these are activities that you enjoyed together. You might also find that your own schedule is suddenly overbooked because you are running errands or attending to other matters on behalf of your depressed friend or family member.

Becoming a good partner

Rosen and Amador make the following recommendations for being a good partner of a depressed person:

- Have realistic expectations. This applies to what you expect from your partner as well as to what you expect from yourself. Remember that you do not have superpowers and cannot 'cure' your loved one's depression. Recovery happens over time and with proper treatment. Be careful not to place unrealistic expectations on your loved one either. Recreating situations that used to make them happy and expecting the same response while they are depressed is a recipe for disaster.

- Try not to take the depression personally. This closely follows having realistic expectations. You did not cause your loved one's depression. In the same way that you cannot wave a magic wand and cure the depression, it is also not your fault.

- Offer unqualified support. Caregivers often encounter a paradox around offering support. It is not unusual for the depressed person to turn down the support that is offered and, in addition, to accuse the caregiver of being too pushy. While research shows that depressed people want help, it also shows that they often turn down direct offers of support. Your depressed loved one may ask for help indirectly, for example by wanting you to just listen to their problems rather than offering ideas on how to solve them. There are two things I'd suggest that you do here. First, keep the channels of communication open. Let your depressed loved one know that you are there to help, but don't insist. And, second, stay in touch with your feelings. It is normal to feel rejected, frustrated and even angry when you are turned away. Find support (a therapist or group for example) for yourself to help in processing these feelings, so you don't end up taking them out on your depressed loved one.

- Share your feelings. If your friend or family member was not depressed, wouldn't you share how you were feeling with them? There is a myth that somehow if you talk about how you are feeling, you will overly burden your depressed loved one. In fact, the opposite is true. If you suddenly stop talking about how you are feeling, your depressed friend or family member may feel like they are 'broken' or not normal. You should continue communicating in the same way that you did before.

- Maintain your routine as much as possible. This is a challenge for most carers because of the additional time and energy (mental and physical) involved in supporting a depressed loved one. As far as is possible, you should stick to your regular routine. This means keeping up at work, seeing friends, exercising. Your best protection against becoming depressed yourself is not to allow someone else's depression to consume you.

- Ask for help. Depression feeds on isolation. In addition to helping ensure that your loved one has the right team of health care professionals, support from other friends and family members and group support, ensure you have the same for yourself.

- Work as a team with your partner. Depression is divisive. You and your friend or family member are on the same side, so stick together. During treatment and recovery, talk openly about working as a team. Team work can mean discussing a new approach to problem solving, or how to adapt to your respective new roles as caregiver and recipient of care – or just sharing feelings. This collaboration can enrich your relationship beyond helping to counter the impact of the depression.

What is depression?

Depression is a common experience. We have all felt 'depressed' about a friend giving us the cold shoulder, misunderstandings in our marriage, or tussles with teenage children. Sometimes we feel 'down' for no reason at all.

However, depression can become an illness when the mood state is severe, if the feelings last for two weeks or more, or if it interferes with our ability to function at home or at work.

To detect a depressed mood, clinicians at Sydney's Black Dog Institute suggest looking for the following signs:

- lowered self-esteem (or self-worth)

- change in sleep patterns, that is, insomnia or broken sleep

- changes in appetite or weight

- reduced ability to control emotions such as pessimism, anger, guilt, irritability and anxiety

- emotions varying throughout the day, for example feeling worse in the morning and better as the day progresses

- reduced capacity to experience pleasure – you can't enjoy what's happening now, nor do you look forward to anything with pleasure. Hobbies and interests drop off

- reduced pain tolerance – you are less able to tolerate aches and pains and may have a host of new ailments

- changed sex drive – absent or reduced

- poor concentration and memory – some people are so impaired they think they are demented

- reduced motivation – it doesn't seem worth the effort to do anything; things seem meaningless

- lowered energy levels.

Bear in mind that there are other diseases that can produce these symptoms. This is one of the key reasons that you want to encourage your friend or family member to involve their general practitioner, primary physician or other qualified health care professional.

Famous people who have suffered from depression

- Buzz Aldrin – astronaut

- Ernest Hemingway – author

- JK Rowling – author

- Sheryl Crow – musician

- John Valder – President, Liberal Party of Australia; Chairman, Sydney Stock Exchange

- Winston Churchill – former British Prime Minister

- Brooke Shields – actress

- Pat Cash – Wimbledon tennis champion

- Woody Allen – film director

- Garry McDonald – actor

- Jim Carrey – actor

- Geoff Gallop – former WA Premier

- Susie O'Neill – Australian Olympic swimmer

- Ewan McGregor – actor

- Nadia Comaneci – Olympic gymnastics champion

- Abraham Lincoln – former American President

Having depression does not need to stop anyone from having a fulfilling life and being successful. If ignorant 'friends' make disparaging remarks about your loved one, you might let them know that being depressed is nothing to be ashamed of, and many highly successful people have suffered from depression too.

Types of depression

The Black Dog Institute believes there are three broadly different types of depression, each with their own features and causes: melancholic depression, non-melancholic depression, and psychotic depression. There may be a fourth type, atypical depression.

Knowing that there are different types of depression is important because each type responds best to different treatments.

Depression can also be sub-typed into 'unipolar' and 'bipolar'. Unipolar depression is the name given when only depressive episodes are experienced. Bipolar depression refers to having highs as well as depressive episodes in between. In the case of bipolar, the depression could be any of the above four types, however researchers at the Black Dog Institute have found that it is most likely to be of a melancholic or psychotic type.

Melancholic depression

Melancholic depression is the classic form of biological depression. Its defining features are psychomotor disturbance (usually showing as slowed or agitated physical movements and slowed cognitive processing abilities) combined with a more severe depression than is the case with non-melancholic depression.

Melancholic depression is a relatively uncommon type of depression. It affects only 1–2 per cent of Western populations. The numbers affected are roughly the same for men and women.

This type of depression has a low spontaneous remission rate. It responds best to physical treatments (for example, antidepressant drugs) and only minimally (at best) to non-physical treatments such as counselling or psychotherapy.

Non-melancholic depression

Non-melancholic depression essentially means that the depression is not melancholic, or, put simply, it is not primarily biological. Instead, it has to do with psychological causes, and is very often linked to stressful events in a person's life, on their own or in conjunction with the individual's personality style. Non-melancholic depression is the most common of the three types of depression. It affects one in four women and one in six men in the Western world over their lifetime.

Non-melancholic depression can be hard to accurately diagnose because it lacks the defining characteristics of the other two depressive types (namely *psychomotor disturbance* or *psychotic* features). Also in contrast to the other two types, people with non-melancholic depression can usually be cheered up to some degree.

People diagnosed with non-melancholic depression will have experienced a depressed mood and social impairment (for example, difficulty in dealing with work or relationships) for more than two weeks.

In contrast to the other types of depression, non-melancholic depression has a high rate of *spontaneous remission*. This is because it is often linked to stressful events in a person's life, which, when resolved, tend to see the depression also lifting.

Non-melancholic depression responds well to different sorts of treatments (such as psychotherapies, antidepressants and counselling), but the treatment selected should respect the cause (for example stress or personality style).

Psychotic depression

Psychotic depression is a less common type of depression than either melancholic or non-melancholic depression. The defining features of psychotic depression are an even more severely depressed mood than is the case with either melancholic or non-melancholic depression; more severe *psychomotor disturbance* than is the case with melancholic depression; *psychotic* symptoms (either hallucinations or, more commonly, delusions), and strong guilt feelings.

Psychotic depression has a very low *spontaneous remission* rate. It responds only to physical treatments (such as antidepressant drugs).

Atypical depression

Atypical depression is a name that has been given to symptoms of depression that contrast with the usual characteristics of non-melancholic depression. For example, rather than experiencing appetite loss the person experiences appetite increase, and sleepiness rather than insomnia. Someone with atypical depression is also likely to have interpersonal hypersensitivity (that is, expecting that others will not like or approve of them).

The features of atypical depression include:

- the individual can be cheered up by pleasant events

- significant weight gain or increase in appetite

- excessive sleeping

- arms and legs feeling heavy and leaden, and

- a long-standing sensitivity to interpersonal rejection.

Causes of depression

Unlike some other illnesses or disorders, there is no simple explanation for what causes depression.

In general, depression is caused by a mixture of 'pressure' or 'strain', which can be mild or severe, combined with a vulnerability or predisposition to depression, which, too, can range from mild to severe.

For each type of depression, there are likely to be different mixtures of causes. For *psychotic* or *melancholic* depression, physical and biological factors are generally more relevant. By contrast, for *non-melancholic* depression, the role of personality and stressful life events are generally far more relevant.

Genetics

Contrary to the popular view that depression is due to life experiences and/or personality factors, there is strong evidence that genetics are a significant factor in a person's predisposition towards developing depression. The genetic risk of developing clinical depression (the medical term for severe depression) is about 40 per cent. The remaining 60 per cent is due to factors in the individual's environment. Depression is unlikely to occur without significant life events, but the risk of developing depression as a result of some such event is strongly genetically determined.

Biochemical factors

Our knowledge of the human brain is still fairly limited; so we do not know what actually happens in the brain to cause depression. It is likely that with most instances of clinical depression, neurotransmitter function is disrupted. Neurotransmitters are chemicals that carry signals from one part of the brain to the next. There are many neurotransmitters serving different purposes, however three important ones that affect a person's mood are serotonin, noradrenaline and dopamine.

In normal brain function, neurotransmitters jump from one nerve cell to the next, and the signal is as strong in the second and subsequent cells as it was in the first. In people who are depressed, the mood-regulating neurotransmitters fail to function normally, so that the signal is either depleted or disrupted before passing to the next nerve cell.

In *non-melancholic depression*, it is likely that the transmission of serotonin is reduced or less active, whereas in people with *melancholic* and *psychotic* depression, the neurotransmitters noradrenaline and dopamine are more likely to have failed or to be functioning abnormally.

Illness

In a simple sense, illness can lead to depression through the lowered mood we can all experience when we are unwell, in pain or discomfort, confined, and less able to do the things we enjoy. Illness can also change the body's functioning in a way that leads to depression. Even if the illness isn't making us feel down, we might still end up with a depression.

For example:

- It is known that certain cancers can produce a depression – in these cases the person might be quite unaware that they have the disease.

- Certain medical conditions can lead to mania.

- Compromised immune functioning might play a part in the emergence of depression, although further research is needed to establish this link.

Ageing brain

As we age, our brain's capacity (in terms of general functioning) reduces, while certain neurotransmitters, which influence mood state, can become affected. Some elderly people who are developing dementia may, at some stage (often early on), develop a severe depression for the first time. The depression is commonly of a psychotic or melancholic type and is a reflection of the disruption of circuits linking certain basal ganglia and frontal regions of the brain. Sometimes these changes merely reflect an ageing process, particularly in people who are vulnerable to this kind of 'wear and tear'. In others, however, high blood pressure or mini-strokes (often unnoticed by the individual and their family) may contribute.

Gender

Gender is a partial, but incomplete, explanation of why a person develops depression. Essentially equal numbers of men and women develop melancholic depression. However, studies have shown that there is a much greater likelihood of women developing non-melancholic depression than men. There are a number of explanations for this.

- Women are more likely than men to 'internalise' stress, thereby placing them at greater risk of developing depression; additionally, women with unsatisfactory marriages or a number of young children are highly overrepresented among samples of depressed people, suggesting a sex-role component or a reduced ability to seek assistance or support.

- Hormonal factors commencing in puberty may account for the increased likelihood in women of developing anxiety – a precursor to depression – or depression.

- While sex hormone (or biological) differences may create a greater likelihood among women of developing depression, certain social factors are still needed to come into play before depression will be experienced.

Stress

It is important to recognise that nearly every individual can be stressed and depressed by certain events. Most people get over the stress or depression within days or weeks, while others do not.

Past and long-standing stresses can increase the chance of an individual developing depression in later years. An example is an abusive or uncaring parent, which may result in the child developing low self-esteem and thus being vulnerable to depression in adult life.

Most individuals who develop *non-melancholic* depression usually describe an important and understandable life event that occurred before the depression started. The events that are most likely to 'trigger' depression are ones where the individual's self-esteem is put at risk, compromised or devalued. For most adults, self-esteem is closely linked to intimate relationships and other important areas like work. Thus, the break-up of a relationship or a marriage is a very common trigger for depression.

Other individuals develop depression when they feel a sense of shame, such as when they believe they have not lived up to their own or others' expectations, which then results in lowered self-esteem.

Personality

Research at the Black Dog Institute has shown that people with particular personality types are more at risk of developing depression than others. These include people exhibiting:

- high levels of anxiety, which can be experienced as an internalised 'anxious worrying' style or as a more externalised 'irritability'

- shyness, expressed as 'social avoidance' and/or 'personal reserve'

- self-criticism or low self-worth

- interpersonal sensitivity

- perfectionism, or

- a 'self-focused' style.

Those who show signs of the first four factors are at a distinctly greater risk of depression, especially *non-melancholic* depression.

Self-testing for depression

The following is a self-test developed by the Black Dog Institute for identifying possible symptoms of clinical depression.[9]

Please note that while great care was taken with the development of this self-assessment tool, it is not intended to be a substitute for professional clinical advice. While the results of the self-test may be helpful, remember that you should always seek the advice of a qualified health practitioner with any questions you have regarding your health.

If your loved one is reluctant to see a doctor, this test could be a good first step to understand the scope of the problem. The test is available on the Black Dog Institute website (see the Resources section for further details); you can undertake the test online to obtain a score.

Please consider the following questions and rate how true each one is in relation to how you have been **feeling lately** (that is, in the last two to three days) compared to **how you normally feel**.

	Not True	Slightly True	Moderately True	Very True
Are you stewing over things?	☐	☐	☐	☐
Do you feel more vulnerable than usual?	☐	☐	☐	☐
Are you being more self-critical and hard on yourself?	☐	☐	☐	☐
Are you feeling guilty about things in your life?	☐	☐	☐	☐
Do you find that nothing seems able to cheer you up?	☐	☐	☐	☐
Do you feel as if you have lost your core and essence?	☐	☐	☐	☐

Are you feeling depressed?	☐	☐	☐	☐
Do you feel less worthwhile?	☐	☐	☐	☐
Do you feel hopeless or helpless?	☐	☐	☐	☐
Do you feel more distant from other people?	☐	☐	☐	☐

How can depression be treated?

Due to the significant amount of research being carried out on depression treatments, new approaches – ranging from prescription medications to self-help and alternative medicine therapies – emerge constantly.

The key is to encourage your friend or family member to get treatment. It is possible for depression to go away on its own, but there is no guarantee. With the treatment that is available today, there is no reason for anyone to suffer unnecessarily.

A large number of different treatments are available for depression. New treatments (particularly medications) appear regularly. Continuing research means that the evidence for how well a treatment works is always changing too.

Researchers at the Black Dog Institute believe that treatments should be selected according to the particular type of depression a person has. Those types of depression that are more biological in their origins (*melancholic depression* and *psychotic melancholia*) are more likely to need physical treatments and less likely to be resolved with psychological treatments alone. *Non-melancholic depression* appears similarly responsive to physical treatments (antidepressants) and psychological treatments.

Physical treatments[10]

The main physical treatments for depression comprise drug treatments and electroconvulsive therapy (ECT). A third physical treatment with as-yet narrow application is transcranial magnetic stimulation (TMS), which has been one of the research areas at the Black Dog Institute.

Because of its controversial past, many people feel the need to think carefully before having ECT or allowing it to be given to relatives. ECT has a small but important role in treatment, particularly in cases of:

- psychotic depression

- severe melancholic depression where there is a high risk of suicide or the patient is too ill to eat, drink or take medications

- life-threatening mania

- severe post-natal depression.

While there are some short-term side-effects, ECT is relatively safe and, because an anaesthetic is used, not too unpleasant.

A possible alternative to ECT is TMS, a procedure used by neurologists both as a treatment and a diagnostic strategy. A coil is held next to the patient's head and a magnetic field created to stimulate relevant parts of the brain. Unlike ECT, there is no need for a general anaesthetic nor is a convulsion induced.

The evidence in favour of this treatment is not yet in, but it is currently a major area of research. If TMS is shown to be as effective as ECT this would be a distinct advance in the treatment of many mood disorders. No clear evidence about its utility is expected for several years.

Drug treatments

The three groups of drugs most likely to be used for depression are antidepressants, tranquillisers and anti-manic drugs or mood stabilisers.

There are a large number of antidepressants. They have a role in many types of depression and vary in their effectiveness across the more biological depressive conditions.

Selective Serotonin Reuptake Inhibitors (SSRIs), *Tricyclics* (TCAs) and *Irreversible Monoamine Oxidase Inhibitors* (MAOIs) are three common classes of antidepressants. They each work in different ways and have different applications.

Clinicians firmly believe that it is important to find the right antidepressant, as different antidepressants produce different effects and results in different people. If the first antidepressant does not work, it is sensible to move to a different kind of antidepressant. For the biological depressive disorders, broad-action antidepressants are usually more effective.

Tranquillisers can be classified as 'minor' or 'major' tranquillisers. Minor tranquillisers (typically a class of drug called benzodiazepines) are not helpful in depression; they are addictive and can make the depression worse. Major tranquillisers, however, are very useful in treating *psychotic* or *melancholic depression* where the person is not being helped by other medications.

'Anti-manic' drugs or 'mood stabilisers' are of great importance in bipolar disorder. Their use in treating mania makes them 'anti-manic', while their ability to reduce the severity and frequency of mood swings makes them 'mood stabilisers'. Lithium, valproate and carbamazepine are the most common.

It is important to remember that the antidepressants and mood stabilisers are often necessary both to treat the depression that is occurring now, and to make a relapse in the future less likely. Consequently, people may need to continue taking medication for some time after they are better.

A well-informed health professional should be able to use their assessment of the type of depression, its likely causes and their understanding of the person to identify the medication most likely to benefit them.

Finally, being able to decide not to use medication is important too, as some types of depression don't respond to them.

Psychological treatments

There is a wide range of psychological treatments for depression. Some of the main ones are:

- cognitive behaviour therapy (CBT)

- interpersonal therapy (IPT)

- psychotherapy

- counselling, and

- narrative therapy.

CBT, IPT, psychotherapy, counselling and narrative therapy all provide either an alternative to medication or work alongside medication. As always, a thorough assessment of the person is needed in order to decide on the best set of approaches.

Cognitive behaviour therapy (CBT)

People suffering from depression – particularly 'non-melancholic depression' – will often have an ongoing negative view of themselves and the world around them. This negative way of thinking is often not confined to depression, but is an ongoing part of how the person thinks about life. Many or all of their experiences are distorted through a negative filter and their thinking patterns become so entrenched that they don't even notice errors of judgment caused by thinking irrationally.

CBT aims to show people how their thinking affects their mood and to teach them to think in a less negative way about life and themselves. It is based on the understanding that thinking negatively is a habit, and, like any other bad habit, can be broken. CBT is conducted by trained therapists either in one-on-one therapy sessions or in small groups. 'Homework' may also be assigned between sessions. Between six and 10 sessions may be required, although the number will vary from person to person.

Interpersonal therapy (IPT)

The causes of depression, or our vulnerabilities to developing depression, can often be traced to aspects of social functioning (work, relationships, social roles) and our *personality*. Therefore, the underlying assumption of interpersonal therapy is that depression and interpersonal problems are interrelated. The goal of interpersonal therapy is to understand how these factors are operating in the person's current life situation, leading them to become depressed and putting them at risk of future depression. Usually 12–16 sessions of IPT are required.

Psychotherapy

Psychotherapy is an extended treatment (ranging from months to years) in which a relationship is developed between the therapist and the patient. The relationship is then used to explore aspects of the person's experience in great depth. The supportive relationship between therapist and patient, and working on understanding the link between past and present, are thought to resolve the depression and make the person less vulnerable to becoming depressed again.

Counselling

Counselling encompasses a broad set of approaches and skills that aim to help an individual explore problems and preferred scenarios. Counselling helps people with long-standing problems in the family or at work, as well as sudden major problems (crisis counselling).

Narrative therapy

Narrative therapy is a form of counselling based on understanding the 'stories' that people use to describe their lives. The therapist listens to how people describe their problems as stories and helps the person to consider how the stories may restrict them from overcoming their present difficulties. It sees problems as being separate from people and assists the individual to recognise the range of skills, beliefs and abilities that they already have (but may not recognise) and that they can apply to the problems in their lives.

Narrative therapy differs from other forms of therapy in that it puts a major emphasis on identifying people's strengths, highlighting evidence of mastering problems in the past. It seeks to build on people's resilience rather than focus on their negative experiences.

The information in this section is based on material from the Black Dog Institute, University of New South Wales, Sydney, Australia, and is used with permission.

Lifestyle factors

Lifestyle factors such as exercise, diet and relaxation techniques can also be extremely helpful in treating depression. There are compelling reasons why these strategies should be part of everyone's treatment plan.

Exercise

Interestingly, of the 289 people interviewed for this book, exercise was rated the most effective treatment for depression; and in a study undertaken by the Black Dog Institute, respondents listed exercise as the second most effective treatment for depression. Despite this, there is very little research that looks specifically at exercise in treating depression.

A study by Dr Andrea Dunn found that patients who did the equivalent of 35 minutes' walking, six days per week, found their levels of depression reduced by 47 per cent.[11] This study, conducted at the Cooper Research Institute in Dallas, Texas, shows that as little as three hours of regular exercise a week reduces the symptoms of mild to moderate depression as effectively as Prozac and other antidepressants.

The anecdotal feedback and studies mentioned above confirm the benefits of exercise. Furthermore, it's a treatment strategy that is accessible to everyone. So why don't people embrace this information and exercise more? As I know all too well, when you are in the black hole you lack the energy and motivation. It's difficult to get out of bed, let alone to exercise. This overwhelming feeling of lethargy can be very difficult to shift. Many people also cite lack of time as a reason for not exercising regularly.

Nearly everyone I have spoken to has experienced supreme difficulty exercising while depressed – although not one of these people ever reported feeling worse after a walk. Andrea Dunn's strategy is to commit to exercising each day, beginning with only a very small commitment, and building up gradually. In the beginning you may only walk for 10 minutes at a time. If you aim to increase the time by 10 minutes each week, you'll be walking the recommended 30 minutes per day by the third week.

Interestingly, when time is at a premium, three periods of 10 minutes' exercise per day can have a similar effect to a 30-minute block.

Of course walking is not the only exercise that will yield results. Swimming, running, cycling, aerobics, dancing, rowing, rollerblading and others will all be beneficial.

Aerobic exercise, in particular, improves blood flow and oxygen to the brain. It has the added benefit of releasing endorphins (natural feel-good chemicals) into the body.

The message is clear: start moving. Exercise has only benefits for people with depression. Unlike medication, there are no detrimental side-effects.

Meditation and relaxation

To manage the frantic pace of modern life it is imperative to take time out and still the mind. This can seem very difficult when your mind is swamped with the negative thoughts that accompany depression. Mastering the art of relaxation doesn't happen overnight, but, like most things, improves with regular practice.

There are many relaxation CDs available – your local library may have a selection. It is often best to try a few different ones and see which works best for you. Likewise, there are many different approaches to meditation. Keep experimenting until you find a style that suits.

In his book, *Full Catastrophe Living: How to cope with stress, pain and illness using mindfulness meditation*, Jon Kabat Zinn from the University of Massachusetts Medical Center describes the excellent results he has achieved for stress and anxiety using meditation. Mindfulness meditation is about living in the present moment, neither focusing on the future nor dwelling in the past. Kabat Zinn guides participants through an eight-week course of meditations; in Australia, Openground conducts these courses in Sydney, Canberra, Alice Springs and Perth. See the Resources section for further details.

Drawing on Jon Kabat Zinn's Stress Reduction program, mental health experts Mark Williams, Zindel Segel and John Teasdale developed mindfulness-based cognitive therapy (MBCT). This form of therapy includes simple breathing meditations and yoga stretches to help participants become more aware of the present moment, including getting in touch with moment-to-moment changes in the mind and the body. MBCT includes basic education about depression and several exercises from cognitive therapy that show links between thinking and feeling. The aim is teaching participants how best to look after themselves when depression threatens to overwhelm them.

MBCT has been used as a relapse prevention strategy with encouraging results. Research undertaken showed that people who had suffered three or more episodes of depression before learning the practice reduced their relapse rate to 36 per cent compared to a relapse rate of 78 per cent in the control group.

The Black Dog Institute is currently involved in trials to evaluate how MBCT can help those in the midst of a depressive episode. Anecdotal feedback is encouraging. The Mindcare Centre also runs MBCT courses; see the Resources section for details.

Nutrition

The importance of eating whole healthy foods with minimum fats and processed sugars cannot be overestimated. The Western way of eating is far from perfect. Cardiac and diabetes problems are ballooning in the West, and we seem to have lost the basics of good nutrition.

In his book *The Great Australian Diet*, Dr John Tickell discusses the eating habits of some of the most vital and longest living people in the world, the Okinawan people of Japan. Along with other Eastern cultures, the Okinawan diet is very high in vegetables, fruits and grains (comprising 85 per cent of their diet) and fish (10 per cent). Meat, poultry and dairy come a distant third (5 per cent). Although it is very hard to make direct comparisons because of cultural and health care delivery differences, the proportion of Japanese people living with depression is much lower than that of Australians.

In her book *Prozac Not Potatoes*, Kathleen DesMaisons PhD, an addiction and nutrition expert, claims that many people who are prone to depression are also sugar-sensitive. This means that their body chemistry reacts in extreme ways to sugar and refined carbohydrates. This changes not only the blood sugar levels, but also the levels of serotonin and beta-endorphins in the brain, creating feelings of exhaustion, hopelessness and despair.

DesMaisons recommends eating three main meals a day and consuming mainly complex carbohydrates such as vegetables, whole grain foods and cereals. She also advocates reducing or eliminating refined sugars (including alcohol) and restricting daily protein consumption to a serve no larger than your fist.

What works in overcoming depression?

There have been countless studies which look at the effectiveness of antidepressants and psychological counselling in treating depression. The problem with this, in my view, is that these studies often don't take into account highly important external factors such as the emotional support someone is receiving, how much exercise they are getting, and how happy they are in their work. With the help of research firm Ultrafeedback, we surveyed 289 people and asked them what they found most effective in treating depression, with 1 = very ineffective and 5 = very effective. What became evident from the research results was that eight out of the top 10 treatments were 'self help' strategies. And, with carers coming in at number two, it also confirmed how important carers are in recovery.

Our results were:

Strategy or Treatment	Number Who Used This Strategy	Average Rating
1. Exercise	252	3.85
2. Support of family and friends	254	3.84
3. Counselling therapies (CBT, IPT, etc)	258	3.69
4. Fulfilling work	220	3.69
5. Relaxation/meditation	235	3.63
6. Nutrition	252	3.56
7. Alcohol and drug avoidance	198	3.56
8. Prescription medicine	258	3.51
9. Support groups	173	3.45
10. Religious or spiritual belief	176	3.18

Coincidentally, at the same time that Ultrafeedback were completing their research, the Black Dog Institute was completing a similar assessment of treatments for depression. Altogether, 2692 visitors to their website judged the effectiveness of different options. This survey didn't look at some of the lifestyle factors that ours did, but it did break prescription medicines down into different categories based on the active chemical components.

Full details of these two research projects can be found in *Back from the Brink* or free online at www.IamBackFromTheBrink.com.

BLACKDOG INSTITUTE

Top 10 treatments for depression[12]

Strategy	Description of strategy	Number Who Used This Strategy	Average 'Effectiveness' Score[*]
1. Venlafaxine	An SNRI[a] medication. Brand names include: Efexor, Efexor XR	672	1.73
2. Exercise		2141	1.70
3. Cognitive behaviour therapy (CBT)	A type of psychological therapy	1221	1.63
4. Other psychotherapy		1181	1.59
5. Interpersonal therapy (IPT)	A type of psychological therapy	700	1.58
6. Escitalopram	An SSRI[b] antidepressant medication. Brand names include: Lexapro	185	1.55
7. Citalopram	An SSRI b medication. Brand names include: Cipramil, Celexa	600	1.51
8. Yoga/meditation		1215	1.47
9. Sertraline	An SSRI b medication. Brand names include: Zoloft	1043	1.47
10. Counselling		1754	1.46

*This average 'effectiveness' score differs from the Ultrafeedback 'average rating'

a) An SNRI antidepressant is a 'serotonin and norepinephrine reuptake inhibitor', which affects the two neurotransmitters serotonin and norepinephrine.

b) An SSRI antidepressant is a 'selective serotonin reuptake inhibitor', which affects the neurotransmitter serotonin.

I felt the final piece of the puzzle was to ask experienced carers what they believed they could do which was most helpful in managing their loved ones' depression. Below are the results from 252 respondents.

Communicating regularly and reassuring them of my love	85%
Encouraging them to see a doctor	78%
Encouraging them to exercise	73%
Encouraging them to see a psychologist	73%
Hugging them	73%
Encouraging them to get out of bed each morning	71%
Encouraging them to relax eg yoga, meditation, hobbies	62%
Encouraging them to find fulfilling work	59%
Nothing I do seems to help	57%
Encouraging them to see a natural therapist	23%

With all three sets of results, it's clear that there is no one strategy that seems superior to the others. The results seem to show, and interviews I held for this book tended to confirm, that a multiple-strategy approach to treating depression will get the best results.

What really, *really* works?

A lot of information has been shared in this chapter. You will have gathered that the term depression covers myriad variants and that there are also a number of treatment options. Although not a mental health professional, through my own journey and after interviewing hundreds of people with depression, I have some definite thoughts about depression and recovery. They include:

1. The reasons for every individual's depression are unique, as are the symptoms they experience.

2. Everyone's path to recovery is different – there is no golden bullet.

3. Because of point 2 above, you cannot rely on a single approach. Multiple strategies are recommended.

However, there are certain trends from the various surveys mentioned above that can't be ignored if a person is serious about overcoming depression.

Exercise: Clinical studies show that 35 minutes' walk (or equivalent) six days per week has a significant positive impact on mood. While many professionals regard exercise highly, I believe it is the MOST important thing you can do. There are only positive side effects.

Seeing a doctor: If your loved one suffers from the depression symptoms reported earlier in this chapter for two weeks they should see a doctor – with no exceptions. When researching this book, we asked experienced carers what they know now that they wish they had known when their loved one initially became depressed. By far the most common response was that they would INSIST on getting an accurate diagnosis earlier.

It is very hard to argue with experience. A skilled doctor will help determine if psychological counselling and/or medication is required. Many carers complain that their loved one refuses to see a doctor; strategies to address this are discussed in Chapter 7.

Emotional support: While many carers report being criticised by the depressed person, often this is a reflection of someone in pain lashing out at those closest to them. The truth is that having emotional support during this very difficult time is irreplaceable. This support can come from family, friends, and support groups. Carers should encourage their loved one to reach out to others so that they don't shoulder all of the burden. There is more on this topic in Chapter 7.

When I did a depression outpatient program, we were encouraged to schedule two to three visits with loved ones in a week. Although you often don't feel like a visit, in the majority of cases I felt better for having had the connection.

Psychological counselling: If your loved one has irrational beliefs or dysfunctional relationships, either cognitive behaviour therapy (CBT) or interpersonal therapy (IPT) may be warranted. Irrational beliefs lead to counterproductive results. It's like an accountant believing that two plus two equals five, yet being surprised that the reconciliation doesn't balance. Likewise some difficult relationships can contribute to depression and can be helped with various forms of counselling.

Other lifestyle: Meditation or relaxation, good nutrition, and alcohol and drug avoidance should all be pursued.

Weekly goals: It is very important to encourage your loved one to set realistic (but not easy) weekly goals for the above strategies. When they set these targets, you should also encourage them to actually schedule in advance when they plan to exercise, meet with family and friends, and relax. This provides a sense of achievement which helps with self-esteem. It is not the end of the world if the goals aren't achieved, but they should be encouraged to reset goals for the next week. For further details on how I applied this in my recovery see *Back from the Brink* or download a free extract from www.IamBackFromTheBrink.com.

As a carer, you have the potential to influence how your loved one responds to their depression and to the issue of treatment. Depressed people often genuinely believe they are beyond help. I have seen in many situations that it is real stories – stories of others battling and overcoming depression – that will eventually move someone with depression to take action. For this reason I highly recommend that they read some of the inspiring stories in *Back from the Brink.*

And my final advice: Learn. Understand. Act.

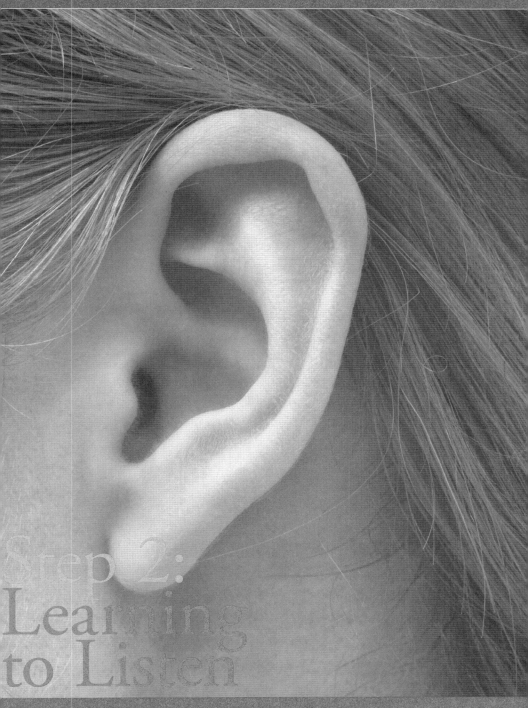

Step 2:
Learning
to Listen

Step 2: Learning to Listen

LISTENING IS A learned skill, not an innate behaviour. When two people are talking, ideally they should share responsibility for good communication. Unfortunately, when someone is depressed it usually severely impacts on their capacity to participate in conversations as they normally would. So here we are going to focus on the things that you, the carer, can do to make up for their deficiencies.

While our wonderful brains are capable of listening to about 300 words per minute, we can only speak at a rate of about 150 words per minute. That gives us lots of free time to do something other than listen. This can make us less-than-great listeners, without us ever intending to be that way.

You see it fairly often: someone is so caught up in what they are going to say next that they actually don't listen to what the speaker is saying.

What about nonverbal communication? Important as they are, words account for only about 7 per cent of the total communication picture; tone of voice accounts for about 38 per cent and body language for about 55 per cent.

Our body language consists of two categories: gestures, which depend on the culture you grew up in; and facial expressions, which turn out to have universal meaning for all humans – part of our evolutionary development.

Some people say that they rely on their intuition – on a gut feeling – to help them fully understand what another person is communicating. This is probably not a good idea. Why? First of all, it can distract you from actually listening (too much noise going on inside your own head). And second, it is not reliable because your intuition is filtered through your own past experiences, prejudices, expectations and a host of other things including:

- your beliefs about the world and what you value

- your nature and attitude to the subject you're hearing about, and

- the culture you grew up in or are part of.

Also, bear in mind that in most Western cultures, being the person speaking is associated with being in a position of power. Depending on your personality, it can be difficult to adopt what may seem like the more passive role of listener. But as I suggested in Chapter 4, knowledge is power – and listening is the key to gaining knowledge (and understanding).

It is often helpful when talking about what makes someone a good listener to consider the traits that make someone a bad listener. We've all been the victim of a bad listener from time to time. This is the person who:

- interrupts us and finishes our sentences

- insists on one-upmanship – no matter what we say, they have been there, done that and know better

- fancies themselves a mind reader and tells us what we are thinking (and what it means) before listening to what we actually have to say

- is obviously distracted or, in the worst cases, ignoring us

- doesn't maintain eye contact, and

- fidgets as if they are waiting for the first opportunity to flee the scene.

So how can you be a good listener, and how can listening skills help you as a caregiver for a depressed friend or family member?

What does good listening look like?

Good listening is learning how to ask better questions.

Just as we have all encountered bad listeners, we've all experienced what it feels like when someone is really listening to us. It is a wonderful feeling, to be heard. Good listeners show the following traits:

- maintain good eye contact

- able to focus on content, not on how it is delivered

- attentive to their own emotions, and take care not to let them detract from what the speaker is trying to communicate

- not easily distracted. Good listeners say that sometimes they will repeat what they are hearing in their mind to help keep them engaged

- understand their own communication style and modify their personal style as appropriate to make the speaker feel more at ease

- authentic, and

- non-judgmental and don't feel obligated to give feedback. They understand that sometimes it is just best to listen. Period.

Who starts the conversation?

The simple answer is 'either of you'.

While withdrawal is a symptom of depression and many people suffering from depression find it difficult to articulate and talk about what they are feeling, not everyone will respond this way. There is no 'one size fits all' with depression.

Let's talk first about initiating a conversation with someone who is depressed and withdrawn. The best place to start is to be authentic to the relationship you already have with your depressed friend or family member. If you would normally say, 'How's it going?' or talk about the outcome of a sporting event or ask if they watched a television program you both like, start there. Don't worry about what you'll say next. Let the depressed person respond. Listen to what they say.

> *It is very destructive to try and minimise my feelings. Please don't cut me off or attack me. Try to understand how frustrated I am.*

What about the person who talks non-stop about their depression? Some depressed people can develop an almost obsessive focus on things or topics – such as what caused their depression or what might cure it. They may strike us as being self-absorbed. Our normal inclination is to write this off as an undesirable personality trait. We might want to get away so we don't have to listen to the same tale of woe again and again and again. Being self-absorbed is, however, part of the illness and there is nothing the depressed person can do about it, any more than they could grow another arm if they lost one!

Someone who is depressed may go from person to person talking incessantly about the suffering they are experiencing. They are seeking comfort, understanding and relief from their illness. It can be very wearing on the network of caregivers to hear this type of conversation. If your depressed family member or friend has reacted to their depression this way, you will need to develop patience as well as good listening skills. The worst thing is for the depressed person to sense that they are being rejected.

Depression will affect how your friend or family member communicates. Try not to be dismayed or take it personally. If my leg were broken, you would not be mad at me or feel hurt if I turned down your invitation to take a run. It's a silly example but you get the point.

Talking about 'it'

> *Don't be afraid of it. Don't always refer us to professionals – sometimes we just want to talk to you about it.*

Your conversation about depression (or just feelings) is likely to depend on whether or not your loved one has already been diagnosed with depression or not.

If you suspect your loved one is suffering from depression but neither you nor they know for sure, the first step is for you to become familiar with the symptoms of depression – we talked about this in Chapter 4.

Remember that knowing the list of symptoms does not make you a therapist or qualify you to render a diagnosis. In our zeal to help a friend or our family member, we have to be careful not to get carried away. We need to remind ourselves to leave those things that require specific medical or psychiatric expertise to the medical and psychiatric experts.

Say you notice that something is not quite right with your loved one and you have started observing symptoms that could be depression. What can you do? The best thing is to share – in a gentle but honest way – what you have observed, and the concerns you might have about what you are seeing. Again, you want to leverage the relationship you already have with the person.

You could start by asking them how they are feeling. If you get the cursory 'everything is fine' answer, tell them you are glad to hear that, but that you have some concerns about what you've been observing lately and that you'd like to share them. Stick to what you have observed rather than speculating on causes for the behaviour. For example, 'I noticed that you are not seeing much of your friends lately, which isn't like you. Are you okay?' or 'You don't seem to have been in the garden for weeks. Is everything okay?'

Let them know that you care, that you believe that they deserve to feel good, and that there are easily accessible resources they might want to make use of as a first step. This could be something as simple as taking an anonymous depression screening test online such as the one on the Black Dog Institute's website (see the Resources section for details) – or it could be making an appointment with a health care professional.

> *Be patient, strong, positive, and listen.*

Don't be surprised if your friend or family member rebuffs your initial suggestion. However, you have expressed what you have been observing; you

have let them know that you care for them and are looking out for their best interests and that there is help available. This may be a conversation you have more than once. Don't be frightened to revisit the conversation in a few days if it is obvious things aren't improving.

The same techniques apply if your loved one has already been diagnosed with depression: it is still important to relate to the person in the way you have been used to doing. Just be aware that their response is quite possibly going to be different than how they would have responded before the depression set in. It may be more difficult than normal for you to communicate and to understand what your depressed loved one is feeling and experiencing.

The best response is to be supportive. You may not be able to fix what is going on for your friend or family member, but you can let them know you are there and that you care. Adopt an 'ask, don't tell' approach to your communication.

Ask me how you can help – don't tell me.

If your depressed loved one does express how they are feeling, be careful not to negate their feelings. For example if the depressed person says, 'I've made a mess out of my life', tell them that you are sorry they feel that way and ask if there is something you can do to help them – rather than telling them that they are wrong.

The best thing to do is to ask the depressed person how you can support them right now, or how you can be of help. If they don't come up with an answer – which is not unusual when someone is depressed – try suggesting an errand or chore around the house that you'd be happy to do for them. Ask them if they would like to take a walk or maybe go for a drive. Depressed people need comfort and understanding. They often feel overwhelmed, so helping them with daily tasks can alleviate stress and can give them a greater sense of control and normalcy. Encouraging them to participate in activities that are fun and low-stress – like a walk, an uplifting movie or a meal – can give them respite from the weight of their illness.

The same things that would make each of us feel cared for or cheer us up can also have a positive impact on the person who is suffering from depression. As a caregiver, you may not immediately observe a difference, though. Your depressed friend or family member may seem as depressed as ever after your walk, meal or conversation.

A big part of us believing that we have communicated successfully depends on how the person we're communicating with responds to us. If you are the carer for a depressed friend or family member, please bear in mind and prepare yourself that this will not be the case during the time that your loved one suffers from depression: you might not get positive feedback, or indeed any feedback at all, when you communicate.

You need to keep reminding yourself that your support does have a positive impact even when there is no direct response. Trust that your support is a vitally important part of your loved one's recovery, even if they are not able to tell you so.

What are they feeling?

> *Talk to your partner. Don't expect a depressed person to seek out communication or to open up a subject.*

Being able to figure out what another person is feeling is an important part of the human experience. This can be especially difficult for the carer if the depressed friend or family member is uncommunicative, is unable to articulate their feelings or tells the caregiver they are feeling a certain way that does not seem in agreement with what the caregiver might have been observing.

Gauging the emotional state of another person is so important that it is actually part of our physical makeup. We all do this naturally, although some

psychologists have taken it to another level, watching people's faces for 'micro expressions' that 'leak' people's true feelings for fractions of a second. With training, it is possible to tell what emotion a person is experiencing even when they're trying to mask the emotion.[13] However being able to identify the emotion does not mean you will understand why the person is experiencing it.

People – depressed or not – are most likely to share their emotions when they feel safe, and with those they trust. If you have found yourself in the role of caregiver, chances are you may already have the trust of your depressed loved one. Hopefully this will lead to an open and honest dialogue about how your friend or family member is feeling and how they are dealing with their depression.

When I asked my psychiatrist, Dr Robert Fisher, how he ascertains how a patient is really feeling, he gave me some interesting insights. He looks first into a person's eyes to see if there is any spark and if they can hold his gaze. He notices their grooming or lack of it. What they do with their hands is also important: unease is often accompanied by wringing of hands. All this, combined with what the patient is actually saying, helps him to make an assessment.

In order to understand how a person is feeling it can also be beneficial to ask them how they are feeling on a scale of 1 to 10, where 1 is actively suicidal and 10 is 100 per cent normal. This can help you understand the gravity of the situation. It is handy to check in on this scale on a regular basis to determine progress. Do this maybe once a week, but more regularly if you sense the potential for self-harm.

Some thoughts on communication between genders

When reviewing the research I did for this book I was overwhelmed by the number of women who expressed supreme frustration at not being able to talk openly to their male partner about depression. A lot has been written about the different ways that the sexes think and communicate. Thinking about this topic brought back vivid memories about my reluctance to talk about my depression with family just before my first suicide attempt.

How to discuss depression with a man

While it is always dangerous to make generalisations, I offer the following guidelines about discussing depression with men.

1. **Men are socialised to be self-sufficient.** I remember my wife being totally perplexed and wondering why I had not discussed my absolute despair with her prior to making an attempt on my life. The truth was that I believed I should be able to solve my own crisis. Real men are supposed to do that … aren't they? Be sensitive to the male ego. Accept that for many men it is very hard to talk about emotions and feelings of doubt and inadequacy. It is best to talk about behaviour rather than threaten his self-esteem. For example, you could say, 'I 'm concerned about you waking up at 4am and not being able to get back to sleep. I want you to know that I love you and I don't want you to feel under any pressure to discuss it now, but I want you to know that I'm here if you want to talk about anything that you could be worrying about.'

2. **Try multiple choice.** In *When Someone You Love is Depressed*, Rosen and Amador suggest that if a man has difficulty discussing feelings, he may respond better to multiple choice. For example, 'Are you feeling worried, sad, or angry right now?' I think this is sound advice.

3. **Affirm their competence.** Again, remember the male ego. You could say, 'I have always been impressed with how well you have managed so many things. I know at the moment you seem to be having some difficulty and I was wondering if there was anything I could do to ease your load?'

4. **Engage in problem solving through asking the right questions.** Let him appear to be in control. You could say 'I know you have many pressures on your time at the moment, what are the things that are causing you to lose sleep? Why does that worry you so much? What do you think can be done

about it? Have you considered asking someone else for help/advice?' If they are struggling to come up with answers, then this might be the time to suggest strategies or someone they could talk to.

How to discuss depression with a woman

Research shows that women are far more likely to discuss their depression with a doctor and/or a partner. Nevertheless, John Gray, author of *Men are from Mars, Women are from Venus* and Rosen and Amador provide some good insights for men, when they are endeavouring to help.

1. **Stop trying to problem solve unless invited.** Women like to feel heard and understood. They do not think as much about problem solving as men. You need to concentrate on her experiences with depression. You could say 'When you say you're a failure at your job, what makes you say that?'

2. **Remember she is an individual.** You could say 'What does depression feel like for you? Why do you think you feel that way?'

3. **Empathise with her.** You could say 'I remember when I took on that new role and feeling absolutely swamped and thinking I would never be a success at it.'

4. Only offer suggestions after she feels certain she has been listened to.

Boundaries

> *They should not expect to take any crap but they should also realise that it is often the 'depression' talking, and not take it personally.*

Setting healthy boundaries is an important part of any relationship. I'm sure more than one of you were admonished, 'I'm your mother, not your friend!' at some point during your adolescence.

We all encounter life events that necessitate altering the nature of our boundaries with another person or group of people. This could include removing boundaries, adding them or perhaps smaller changes. Illness is one such life event. And depression is an illness.

Most people experience change as somewhat uncomfortable. It doesn't feel right to us. It's like the new shoe that is a bit bothersome until we get used to it. Caregivers often find that they must deal with changes related to their relationships and helping the depressed person figure out what might now constitute healthy boundaries.

For example, your loved one may snap at you when you ask them to do a job around the house, which is totally out of character. It's all right to say politely but firmly 'I know you are not feeling well at the moment, but it is not acceptable to be rude to me when I ask you to do something. I've had a busy day too and it's important that we still share the load'.

Being aware that the nature of how we react to any change is to resist it is an important first step. The second step is being able to cultivate attentiveness to what you are feeling. Psychologists tell us that most people are not aware of what they are feeling until they start reacting to their emotions. In the case of feeling anger or frustration, it is best if you can be aware of the feelings and process them before you react to them.

If you can maintain an awareness and sensitivity, then figuring out what the new healthy boundaries should look like will be a combination of communication and common sense.

Often setting boundaries is about knowing what to say and what not to say. Let's start with 'what not to say'.

What not to say

When people suffering from depression were surveyed about what information they would like to share with caregivers, one of the most common requests was to help caregivers understand what not to say. Of course, these things will differ from person to person – we all have distinct individual emotional triggers. The closeness of the relationship you have with your family member or friend will determine whether or not you are aware of what those distinct emotional triggers are. If you know what triggers your depressed loved one, try not to use those concepts or words in conversation. And if your friend or family member uses trigger words on you, resist the impulse to react to them. Focus on what the person is trying to communicate to you rather than reacting emotionally to the words.

Here are the most popular things NOT TO SAY to a depressed person:

1. You have a lot going for you. Don't you think being depressed is ungrateful?

2. Don't worry – be happy.

3. It could be worse; people are starving and killing each other elsewhere.

4. Just ignore it, it will go away.

5. If this is the worst thing that ever happens to you, consider yourself lucky.

6. Haven't you been feeling down long enough? When is this going to be over?

7. You are being selfish. What about me/your family/your [FILL IN THE BLANK]?

8. I have problems too.

9. At least you're not really sick, like with cancer or anything.

10. Don't you like me anymore?

11. If you lost weight/got a different job/stopped smoking you wouldn't be depressed anymore.

12. If you'd just do what I tell you, you would get better.

13. Are you going to do something stupid?

133

14. You just need to change your attitude.

And the all-time favourite:

15. Snap out of it!

Boundaries go both ways

> *Explain that we just can't help it. It [depression] takes a hold and won't let go. We might want to isolate ourselves. Let us ... to a point, but also let us know that you are there. It is very difficult to want to be left alone, but also need to know that someone loves you anyway. However bad behaviour is not acceptable and should not be tolerated by [the caregiver]. [They should] look after themselves too ... don't give all to the person with depression.*

Many caregivers don't feel they have the right to set any boundaries for the depressed person, and feel guilty if they do.

However, boundaries go both ways. If you don't have healthy boundaries, you may develop resentment towards your depressed friend or family member. Resentment can lead to neglect or outright hostility – both are outcomes you should seek to avoid.

It is okay to tell the depressed person what you need. Be sensitive to the fact that your depressed loved one may not be able to respond in all the same ways as they might have done prior to the onset of their depression. However, all relationships are based on a mutual meeting of needs – even if 'needs' is a dynamic term. It is still important to share what you are feeling and what you need with your depressed friend or family member.

How do you tell a depressed person that their behaviour is unacceptable?

Don't take any nonsense from us either.

Having read about how disabling and overwhelming depression is, many carers struggle to discuss something that annoys them with a loved one. Often the response is to suffer in silence, which can ultimately lead to resentment and anger. Quite frankly, it is in everyone's interests that the communication channels stay open. Depression can lead to the most overwhelming sadness and despair, but it is no excuse for repeatedly being disrespectful or rude. The following guidelines are based on my own experience and feedback from people with depression and their carers:

- Acknowledge that you understand depression can have a terrible effect on how they think and act.

- When you are highlighting what is bothering you, don't make it a personal attack that could further erode their self-esteem and lead to greater alienation.

- Discuss the issue in terms of behaviour and how that behaviour makes you feel. Stay calm but firm.

You could say 'I know how depression makes you grumpy in the morning and that can make you lash out at me and the children. Yesterday morning, when I reminded you of your doctor's appointment, and you started shouting at us, it made me feel very resentful and it frightened the children. Your depression is not just hard on you, it is hard on the whole family. We can only get through this if we work together. Please don't raise your voice like that again'.

How to be encouraging

> *Appreciate and encourage small steps even if you think it's not much of an achievement, but don't do it in a patronising way – we're depressed, not stupid.*

People who are depressed know – even if they don't articulate this – that you cannot solve their problems. They are not looking for that: they are looking for compassion and understanding as they work to recover from what is a devastating illness. They probably need help finding the right resources as well as support as they go through treatment and recovery. Your depressed friend or family member needs to know and feel on a heart level that you care enough to listen. This is why listening is so important. It is a reflection of what you feel for the person who is depressed.

> *Congratulate me when I do things that help me because shit, it's hard.*

What to say

Encouragement and support are probably the two most important things that caregivers can provide to their depressed loved ones. Stay honest. Remember that being depressed changes how a person views the world around them. It is helpful to have an honest friend or family member who can provide gentle input about their view of what is real and what is not.

It is also important to be consistent. When you are depressed, much of what you used to trust doesn't hold true anymore. You may have lost a job you used to be really good at, may no longer fully relate to a partner you know you love deeply – or at least used to. Even getting up and brushing your teeth in the morning may no longer be a sure thing. As a carer, you need to take care of yourself and not subsume your life to the person who is struggling with depression. That is healthy. Be careful not to make promises that you can't keep so that when you say you will do something, the depressed person can count on it. This can be extraordinarily comforting when all else seems to be piling up around one's knees in a sad heap.

So what to say? My advice would be to listen to your heart as the best guidance. Here are some other things you might want to say, but only if it is true and authentic for you to do so.

- I care about you/love you/you are such a treasured friend.

- I am here if you need me and I'm not going to leave you because of this.

- Would you like to talk about this?

- Can I hug you or hold your hand? Would that make you feel better?

- I know I can't understand what you are going through, but I am here to help you in whatever way works best for you.

- I am so sorry you are in such pain.

Don't give up on your depressed loved one. Keep the channels of communication open.

The power of the written word

The power of the written word shouldn't be underestimated. I have heard several accounts where a person was refusing to engage in conversation about a difficult subject, but later responded after they had received a carefully worded letter about the same subject. The structure of the letter should be guided by the same suggestions listed above for the spoken word.

I felt very uncomfortable discussing my suicide attempt with my children but for some reason found it much easier to explain myself in writing. I believed that raising that subject was important in allowing our relationship to move forward, and that proved to be the case. My psychiatrist always advises his patients to communicate in writing if a communication impasse has been reached or a very difficult subject needs to be raised.

> *They don't have to have all the solutions. One friend said to me: 'I can't do anything, so I'll just hold you tight while you cry'. That was incredibly affirming and the most helpful thing anyone has done.*

Step 3:
Finding the
Right Help

Step 3: Finding the Right Help

> *When I'm in the Black Hole, it doesn't seem remotely possible that I will get well again.*

You can lead a horse to water ...

The nature of depression is that often the depressed person genuinely believes they are beyond help. Additionally, the research for this book showed us that many people, particularly men, are reluctant to seek help. This is compounded by the fact that many men consider it a weakness if they ask for help. I gave some guidance in the previous chapter on how to broach the subject of depression and its symptoms with someone who is unable to admit they are not coping. If they point-blank refuse to seek help despite displaying many of the symptoms of depression, I would encourage them to do an anonymous self-test such as the one on the Black Dog Institute's website (see the Resources section for details).

If they still refuse to see a doctor, you can try another tactic. You could say something like, 'I understand that it is often very difficult to talk about these things and I respect that you are not ready to talk to a doctor. I'm still very concerned about you, though, and would like to discuss what we do next in one week's time if things haven't improved. Are you comfortable with that?'

The breakthrough for these people is when they admit that they aren't coping; sometimes you have to be patient before you hear that admission. When running support groups I have found that often the best way to get that admission is to ask them, 'Does it bother you when you experience [depression symptom]?'

Then say nothing and wait for a response. If they admit they are concerned, I would then say, 'From reading about depression research I know that it is a very treatable condition. Why don't I make an appointment for us to see the doctor?'

Finding the needle in the haystack

Once you are over the initial hurdle of getting your depressed loved one to agree to seek help, there are various options. Initially, it's best to see a general practitioner, who may then refer you on to a psychologist or a psychiatrist. There are also support groups available – for both depressed people and their carers. The final section of this chapter deals with how to find the right help for depressed young people.

General practitioners

Your loved one's general practitioner (GP) is a great place to start the process of finding the right help. If they don't have a GP, or lack confidence in their GP being able to treat depression, the Beyondblue website has a list of GPs who have a special interest in mental health (see the Resources section for details).

Ask them if they would like you to go with them to their appointment. Cognitive ability is often affected by depression and having a third party to ask questions and remember responses can be very helpful. Remember it is the nature of depression for the sufferer to think there is no hope for them, but they may be willing to see a doctor if you accompany them.

To help your depressed loved one prepare for the visit and to make it productive, it may help to think about questions the GP is likely to ask, and take notes. The GP may want to know:

1. What are all the symptoms they are experiencing? For how long?

2. How is it impacting on home and work life? What is the level of disability?

3. Was the episode triggered by any stressful events?

4. What emotional support do they have?

5. Were there any stressful events in their childhood?

6. Is there is a family history of depression?

7. Do they engage in any self-medication, for example drinking alcohol, taking illicit drugs etc?

8. Do they ever feel like harming themselves or someone else?

The visit

You should expect your loved one to receive a thorough assessment of their condition. You should also have an opportunity to ask questions.

If your GP establishes that clinical depression does exist in your loved one, they will generally explore two strategies for treatment – antidepressant medication and/or psychological counselling.

If the GP recommends medication, ask them why they have recommended that one in particular, and what can be expected in taking it. Are there any side-effects? What should you do if the side-effects are too unpleasant?

In addition to these traditional approaches, if the doctor doesn't volunteer it, you might ask: 'Is there anything else they could be doing to help, such as exercise etc?' It is best they have this recommendation from their GP and don't feel it is just you harping on.

Don't leave that first visit without:

1. A plan for the next week.

2. An appointment no more than a week later.

You will need a referral from a GP to see a psychiatrist, and visits to psychologists are now eligible for Medicare rebates if referred by a GP (see below).

Psychologists

Psychologists are health professionals who provide 'talking therapies' (psychotherapy) to treat mental health problems. As highlighted in Chapter 4, the two main therapies for treating depression are cognitive behaviour therapy (CBT) and interpersonal therapy (IPT). CBT looks at changing negative thought patterns and helping the depressed person feel better about themselves. IPT looks at addressing problems the depressed person may be having in their relationships which could be affecting how they feel about themselves.

Choosing a psychologist

A GP is often able to identify a local psychologist that he or she thinks would suit your loved one. There are also sites like www.goodtherapy.com.au which provide a lot more information than the Yellow Pages to help you make a decision. Look at your first visit as a test drive – your loved one must feel confident that the psychologist is capable and effective and that they respect them.

In preparing for a session, you may want to jot down some history notes from the questions outlined for GPs above.

After the first visit, your loved one should consider:

1. Did the session feel worthwhile?

2. Did the psychologist understand their situation?

3. Did the psychologist seem genuinely interested in helping?

4. Did the psychologist outline a plan that they had confidence in?

5. Do they trust the psychologist and want to return?

If, after answering these questions, your loved one doesn't feel comfortable with the psychologist, you should help them find another. Tell your GP why you weren't happy with them and ask for another referral. Once they have experienced one that isn't right for them they should be better equipped to choose one that is.

What is the Better Access to Mental Health Care Initiative?

The Australian government introduced this initiative in November 2006, providing rebates for a range of mental health services which were not previously subsidised. Rebates are now available for psychologists, social workers and occupational therapists. To qualify, a person with depression or anxiety first needs to get a referral from a GP, psychiatrist or paediatrician.

In one calendar year, a person with depression or other mental illness is eligible to receive up to 12 individual consultations (18 in exceptional circumstances) and up to 12 group therapy sessions. The referring GP is to review the person's progress after each block of six visits.

Psychiatrists

Psychiatrists train as medical doctors first and then go on to train in psychological medicine. They are the specialists for mood disorders and your GP may refer you to one to benefit from their greater experience. They are also trained in talking therapies, but rightly or wrongly, are often considered to be quite medication-centric. Having said this, many people receive enormous benefit from medication, and there are certainly advantages in working with a specialist.

There are some psychiatrists who concentrate more on talking and alternative therapies, but these are much harder to find.

Preparing to see a psychiatrist is similar to the way you'd prepare to see the GP. There are advantages in you attending the first session with your loved one (if they are comfortable with this), as it is hard to remember the names of different drugs and their benefits and side-effects. (To help you better understand the different indications for the various drugs, the national depression initiative, Beyondblue, has a very good fact sheet on their website. See the Resources section for details.)

If your loved one has already been on medication, the psychiatrist will want to know what they have tried, what the dose was, if there were any benefits and/or side effects, and why they stopped taking it.

It is important to stress that medication is not an exact science so even if the first medication doesn't work, you should encourage your loved one to keep trying. It is also wrong to expect medication to be a 'magic bullet' as there are many other lifestyle and counselling strategies that can aid recovery. As indicated earlier, you should also be strongly encouraging your loved one to exercise daily and to have regular contact with family and friends.

Support groups

There are a number of different mental health support groups out there that you could encourage your depressed loved one to look into. Some are general in nature while others are much more specific. I am most familiar with GROW so will give a brief overview of it here as an example of how they work. Many of the benefits of GROW also apply to other support groups.

I have been a member of GROW for five years and the organiser of a group for the last two years. GROW is a 12-step recovery program for mental health which was started in Australia in 1957. It evolved out of Alcoholics Anonymous (AA) when a group of patients who had just left a psychiatric hospital received benefit from the support at AA meetings but found the elements surrounding drug dependence not to be relevant.

The group runs for two hours each week and is run by the members. It follows a structure which allows time for problem solving. People are encouraged to raise issues they are having and receive input from the group on what they should do. From that input, the person agrees to do a practical task in the next week which will address the issue, and will be given a relevant part of the GROW program to read. There is also time in the meeting to read and discuss part of the GROW literature. Members are encouraged to call each other between meetings to see how they are going and check progress on their practical task.

The main benefit that members report is meeting people who really understand what they are experiencing. They don't feel so alone. The program works by challenging irrational thoughts, so is quite congruent with the principles of cognitive behaviour therapy. For a better understanding of how GROW works, read Sonia Attard's story in *Back from the Brink* and visit www.grow.net.au.

It is not uncommon for the depressed person to bring a partner, parent, or friend along to their first meeting to give them moral support. Once the person has met the group, it is best if they come themselves and take responsibility for their own recovery. We also suggest that someone attends at least four meetings before deciding whether to join the group as it is very hard to comprehend how it all works in one or two visits.

I have witnessed many recoveries through GROW and would definitely encourage your loved one to look into finding a support group. Many of the people in GROW also see a psychiatrist and/or a psychologist, but find the emotional support and insight they receive through GROW extremely helpful.

Chapter 8 gives some pointers for choosing a support group for yourself.

Finding help for a child or adolescent

There are not a lot of doctors or psychologists who specialise in children's and adolescents' mental health, and I have spoken to several motivated and caring parents who found accessing the right help incredibly frustrating and difficult.

The symptoms for a young person with depression are basically the same as those of adults, but because of the physical and mental changes that teenagers naturally undergo, there are added complications with diagnosis.

WHAT PARENTS CAN DO

All situations are different. When young people are suffering with depression they are not always able to ask for help and may even refuse your help at times. This can be difficult because you feel as if you're being rejected. It is important that you:

- Never treat depression as if it is simply teenage 'blues' – always take it seriously.

- Encourage your child to seek help by providing a list of contacts for them to choose from.

- If your teenager won't ask for help and you are really worried, go to your GP by yourself first and get some advice about how to best handle the situation.

- Show love and concern – this doesn't mean that you have to agree with everything your child does or wants to do, but young people need to know that you still love them no matter who they are or what they do.

- Take time to listen when your teenager wants to talk about their feelings.

- Show them that you are available without being 'pushy'.

- Encourage them to do things you know they enjoy.

- Notice the little things they do such as putting their plate in the dishwasher, and thank them.

- Make sure that you do not keep a gun in your home or shed. (Farmers need to be very careful about where they store guns because this is the suicide method often used by young people in country areas.)

- Take seriously any talk about suicide and actions such as giving away special things. Do whatever is needed to protect your child's safety – even if it is against his or her wishes.

Adapted from the Child Youth Health website: www.cyh.com.

Where to get help

There is a range of different treatments for depression varying from counselling and therapy to group and peer support or a combination of these. Antidepressant medication is not recommended for young teenagers. It may be considered for a young person with melancholic depression, but the incidence of this is very low. You must be guided by your doctor.

The right treatment will depend on the individual's needs and situation. It is important to persist until the right support is found as often young people are particular about who they will talk to.

The following organisations or people may be of some help in either providing treatment or referring you to others who will be able to provide help for your son or daughter. There can be long waiting lists, so when making an appointment do explain briefly what the problem is, especially if you are very worried.

- Child and Adolescent Mental Health Services (CAMHS)

- your doctor

- parentline, a telephone counselling service

- youth health services

- community health centres

- psychiatrists

- psychologists, and

- counsellors specialising in working with depressed young people.

- parents can sometimes be wary about bringing their concerns out

in the open for fear of what others will think. It is important that you don't allow this fear to stop you from getting the best support you need to help your child. It may be hard to find an appropriate counsellor, since there are not many psychologists, psychiatrists or doctors trained in working with teenagers. Although not a substitute for seeing a professional, the internet-based support service MoodGym may be helpful. Developed by the Australian National University, MoodGym can be tailored to suit the needs of each individual.
(See http://moodgym.anu.edu.au.)

Pinpointing the right mental health professional for an adolescent

When I was working as a headhunter, my job was to find the best person to meet a client's specific needs. These people were often difficult to find – which is why the organisations employing us would be happy to pay our hefty fees! When looking for the right mental health professional for your teenager, I'd suggest employing your own headhunting skills. Here's the approach I would take:

- **Compile a list of people who can help you.** Think of people or organisations that may know the right person, or that may know a respected opinion leader who themselves may know the right person. This would include your GP, a clinical person at the local Child and Adolescent Mental Health Service, your child's school counsellor, Parentline, the Beyondblue helpline, the local mental health service 24/7 helpline and so on.

- **Prepare your script.** This is a succinct way of describing the type of person you are seeking. You want a brief one- to two-minute description of the situation and who you are looking for. It is very important to use the name of the person you're speaking to, and be pleasant and not demanding – remember you are seeking their help. In order to get them to start thinking of doctors/psychologists they respect, a non-threatening way to approach this is to ask who they would refer their son or daughter to. You are also seeking to find out why they are recommending that person, and if there is any other person they would also recommend. (This is in case the preferred person is booked out for months.) Your script might go something like this:

Hi Mary, my name is John Smith and my GP, Dr Michelle Brown, suggested you may be able to help me. I have a 12-year-old daughter, Jenny, who appears to be displaying some symptoms of depression. For the last three weeks she has had a lot of difficulty getting out of bed and now hates going to school which is so unlike her. She cries all the time and is particularly hard on herself. She also has had a lot of recent issues with school friends and isn't sleeping well. She is quite shy and reluctant to talk about it. I am trying to find a psychiatrist who is very comfortable talking to adolescents and who will explore psychological and social issues thoroughly before resorting to medication. If you had a daughter experiencing problems like these, I was wondering who would you try and get them an appointment with?

You then listen and probe further.

You mentioned Dr Murphy. What do you like about him? ... If Dr Murphy is booked out for weeks, is there anyone else you would recommend?

Through this process, you will hopefully be given a few names. Then start with the one that you sense is the best option. In non-metropolitan areas, unfortunately, it is highly unlikely that you will find someone with all the qualities you are seeking; you may have to travel to find the help you need.

Getting an appointment

Unfortunately, it is highly probable that the person you are trying to see will be very busy and could be booked out for a while. This is where the receptionist can be your best ally – or the toughest gatekeeper! Remember that she has a difficult and stressful time supporting a very busy doctor or psychologist. Ask for her help. Don't be afraid to stress the urgency of the situation. You may say, for example:

> *Hi Janet, I wonder if you can help me? My name is John Smith and Gwen Reynold, the psychologist at Randwick, thought that Dr Murphy could be very well suited to help my daughter Jenny. My GP, Dr Michelle Brown, thinks that she could be clinically depressed. Jenny has been saying recently that we would be better off without her, and my wife and I are worried sick. When would be the soonest that she could see Dr Murphy?*

She may then tell you that unfortunately things are booked out for a while, in which case I'd suggest a response like this.

> *Is there anything we could do to see him earlier than that? I know that you get cancellations at the last minute. Is there any chance you could let me know first about these cancellations? I don't care how late the notice is.*

If the delay in seeing him is still too great, you may consider asking the receptionist if there is anyone else she would recommend.

Step 4:
Providing the
Best Support

Step 4: Providing the Best Support

IN RESEARCHING THIS book, I spent a great deal of time talking to sufferers of depression and their caregivers and reflecting on the question: what is THE most important component of support?

Personally I believe that there are three nearly equal aspects of support. While it is a close call, one component is more important than the other two: that is helping your friend or family member get an accurate diagnosis for their depressive symptoms and helping them get treatment.

Why is an appropriate diagnosis and treatment the most important component? The simple answer is: because depression is an illness. While it is true that occasionally depression will go away on its own, it is not common for this to happen, or it may take an unacceptable time to occur. If your loved one has not yet been diagnosed and is not yet receiving treatment, then all of your other efforts to provide care are more or less like throwing something against the wall and hoping it sticks. Diagnosis and treatment are really the first steps. And so this is the most important component of support.

The remaining two components of support are providing what I'm calling integrated support, and taking care of yourself. I'll discuss those components later in this chapter.

While these three components are the important 'doing' aspects of care, it is also critical to reassure them of your love and care. Hugs and emotional support should never be underestimated.

> *The most valuable thing a [carer] can do is just let you know that although they don't understand what you are going through that they love you and are here for you.*

When doing research for this book, I asked interviewees what the most helpful strategies have been in supporting their loved one with depression. The answers were as follows.

Communicating regularly and reassuring them of my love	85%
Encouraging them to see a doctor	78%
Encouraging them to exercise	73%
Encouraging them to see a psychologist	73%
Encouraging them to get out of bed each morning	71%
Hugging them	73%
Encouraging them to relax eg yoga, meditation, hobbies	62%
Encouraging them to find fulfilling work	59%
Nothing I do seems to help	57%
Encouraging them to see a natural therapist	23%

Helping someone with diagnosis and treatment

One of the (many) tragedies of depression is that the symptoms of the disease can cause the sufferer to feel like everything is so completely hopeless that there is no treatment in the world that could possibly help them. This leads them to the conclusion: *why bother*? Depression also robs people of their self-esteem to the point where they may not believe they deserve treatment. And many people, once they become depressed, lose their perspective on what is really going on and either ignore or deny that depression might be the issue.

So how do you go about helping someone get an appropriate diagnosis (and subsequent treatment) if they believe that all is lost, or that no treatment would work for them, or that actually nothing is wrong with them and the problem is all in your head?

155

Remember that only a qualified health care professional can diagnose depression. Also that there isn't a simple lab test that can be done – the diagnosis of depression depends on the presence of defined symptoms over a period of time. Please refer to Step 1 for the list of symptoms.

> *When I'm in the Black Hole, it doesn't seem remotely possible that I will get well again.*

I would recommend that you have an open, compassionate discussion with them about what you have observed. Let them know that you are concerned. Suggest that it might be a good idea to explore what is going on and that you are happy to help them do this. You could give them the website for the Black Dog Institute's anonymous online depression screening. You could make an appointment for them with their doctor and offer to go with them. You could share with them what you have learned about depression and recovery. For example, let them know that depression treatment has a high rate of success, especially if research-backed protocols are followed. Gently point out that their feeling that no treatment will help or that they are not worthy to receive treatment is likely to be caused by the fact that they are depressed, rather than being the reality! Tell them that you know they are worth it and that you have hope – hope which is backed up by lots of evidence and the experiences of millions of people.

It is best to avoid telling your friend or family member that you understand how they feel unless you have suffered from depression and gone through recovery yourself. If you have not, you cannot understand what they are going through, as much as you may want to. It is okay to let them know that while you can't understand or feel what they are experiencing, you can see that it is extraordinarily difficult for them. Let them know that you just want to help.

> *Let those family and friends know that it isn't them [we want to shut out] when we want to shut out the world … and most of all, hugs are really important. A touch on the shoulder or arm is reassuring.*

Depending on how resistant your friend or family member is, this discussion might be an ongoing one. Try to be persuasive without being too pushy. The exception to this is if you believe your loved one might hurt themselves or someone else. In this event, you must seek emergency help immediately: in Australia dial the Suicide Callback Service on 1300 659 467 and in the US dial 911 for emergency services.

Supporting someone with bipolar

Bipolar is a type of depression which features lows interspersed with mania or highs. During this period of mania a person with bipolar is euphoric and may do things such as shop extravagantly, start unrealistic projects, be sexually promiscuous, or do something socially embarrassing. This presents some unique challenges to the carer and the following is offered as guidance.

The carer's role during a manic episode moves more to that of a 'teacher' or 'policeman'. During these highs the carer needs to be quite assertive to ensure their loved one doesn't do something that they regret later. It is best to have a discussion when the person is in a stable mood to gain their agreement that it's okay for the carer to act this way when required. There may be circumstances where the person requires hospitalisation and, again, it is best to agree beforehand what warrants this action and, preferably, get this in writing.

- **Have a crisis plan** – when a person is in the throes of mania they rarely recognise their need for help and having a plan in writing for this situation can be persuasive. Consider the need for a power of attorney. Where hospitalisation is desirable, encourage voluntary admission, rather than scheduling.

- **Encourage them to take their medication** – mania is seductive and many people with bipolar are tempted to stop taking medication when in the middle of a high.

- **Consider restricting credit cards** – some families agree that the person with bipolar shouldn't have a credit card to restrict their spending during highs.

- **Recognise early symptoms** – all immediate family should be educated on the nature of bipolar and taught to identify early signs of changes from depression to mania and vice versa.

- **Focus** – encourage them to focus on one task at a time.

- **Support** – let your loved one know that you care. When they are on a high they feel they can take on the world but when negative thoughts begin they need to feel loved.

- **Benefits** – be attuned to the unique positive benefits of mania, eg increased creativity.

Offering integrated support

Caregivers provide intellectual, social, emotional, physical and spiritual support. Carers spontaneously and intuitively integrate the support they provide: their support is not compartmentalised.

Integrated support can be as simple as just listening to your depressed loved one talk about how they are feeling, or affirming that the fact that they could get out of bed and brush their teeth *is* progress and it *absolutely* counts.

Integrated support could be as complex as helping them research the efficacy and side-effects of medication they are considering, or being an advocate for them within the health care system.

Integrated support is a model of how we interact as interconnected beings with healthy boundaries. These interactions are often eroded by the symptoms of depression: in caring for a person with depression you are modelling these interactions in a positive way even if – depending on where your friend or family member is vis-à-vis their treatment and recovery – the interaction seems a bit one-sided at times.

So, what can you do? Below are some of the elements of intellectual, social, emotional, physical and spiritual support that you can offer your depressed loved one. In fact, without even thinking about it, you are probably offering these forms of support already.

Build knowledge

I've talked about building knowledge earlier in the book: it is the first of the Seven Steps. The more you know about depression, the greater help you can be to your depressed friend or family member. Share what you have learned with them and encourage them to learn about their illness. This will help them to feel less powerless as well as help them make informed decisions about treatment with their team of health care professionals.

Help out with the day-to-day

When you are depressed, things that the rest of us might take for granted as being easy aren't necessarily so. Severely depressed people may spend the entire day cajoling and bargaining with themselves just to be able to convince themselves to get out of bed or out of the house once a day. Ask before jumping in, but your friend or family member might really appreciate help with laundry, taking the rubbish out or an offer of childcare while they go for a doctor's appointment.

If your loved one is one of those people who find it difficult to accept help, you might make suggestions here and there. A sink full of dishes or heaps of laundry sitting about are silent hints about where a helping hand might be needed.

Don't be discouraged if offers for help are rejected

People with depression feel particularly inadequate. It might seem to them that if they let someone else do something for them, it will confirm that they are not competent. Don't be discouraged by this and reaffirm your care for them. Next time you meet maybe you could propose some options they can choose from. You might say, 'Next week when I come over, would you prefer it if I prepared a meal or did your washing?'

Encourage physical activity

Clearly if your friend or family member is struggling to get out of bed, suggesting a jog is probably not going to be well received. In that case, see if they are perhaps open to a small change of scenery – it might be just going to the kitchen for a bite to eat or watching television. Take it in baby steps.

If your depressed loved one is up and about more, see if they might like to take a walk with you or some other gentle exercise that they feel they can handle. Research clearly demonstrates that exercise offers physiological benefits that can help alleviate depressive symptoms. Exercise has a positive impact on the same neurotransmitters that antidepressant medications target. It also produces brain chemicals called endorphins which are associated with feelings of wellbeing. And exercise can reduce tension and stress as well as feelings of anxiety – this can help with depression-related insomnia and muscle aches.

Exercise can also help on a psychological level. We perceive exercise as a positive activity – it is good self-care. The simple act of doing something to help ourselves can make us feel productive and in control. If you are able to encourage your friend or family member to do some exercise, this could help counter feelings of worthlessness. I would recommend that you encourage realistic goals around the topic of exercise. People suffering from depression usually also experience extreme, unrelenting fatigue. There are going to be days when they just don't feel like a walk – or much of anything else – and you don't want them to feel like they have failed. Exercise should be an activity that contributes in a positive way to their recovery, rather than being 'another' thing to fail at.

Offer emotional support

We are used to having a natural give and take in our relationships; in fact we depend on it in many cases to let us know how we are doing with the other person. It is reassuring to express an emotion and have it returned in kind. If you are caring for a depressed loved one, chances are that the give and take you are used to will become very one-sided for a while: all give and no take. This can be frustrating. Be prepared.

It is important to be patient, not to judge your depressed friend or family member, and to listen to them. Depressed people need compassion and understanding.

Taking care of yourself

The final component of the best support is for you to take care of yourself. Practising good self-care means that you will:

- put yourself first
- keep up social contacts and avoid allowing yourself to get isolated
- take steps to manage stress associated with caregiving, and
- seek help (no superheroes allowed!).

Good self-care is not an option: it is an *obligation* to yourself that you must fulfill if you are going to take on the role of being a caregiver.

Caregiver self-care is so important that I've dedicated Steps 5 and 6 to this topic.

> *After 13 years of living with my husband I have nothing left to give him. I know we are meant to understand their journey and their issues and their needs and their wants ... but as I write this the anger and resentment inside me is finally bubbling up. Who encourages the partners to go find a yoga class, find fulfilling work or take us to a natural therapist? Who loves and hugs and supports us? Who encourages us to keep going with no support? I have done everything in my power – encouraged my husband to do all the things you have listed below, as a GOOD partner should. Has my help and my support helped him? No. Has it nearly destroyed me? Very nearly. No one EVER asks about how the partners are going – ever. I very much hope you include this reflection in your book, as it will, hopefully, speak to all the other people out there who have not dared raise the courage to say out loud 'what about me.'*

For a comprehensive workbook and other resources that allows you to tailor your communication and care for your loved one visit www.DepressionCarer.com/workbook

Step 5:
Finding
Help for You

Step 5: Finding Help for You

THE ISSUES THAT caregivers face are pretty much consistent across all situations, regardless of the illness the friend or family member is affected by. While these issues can be tough to deal with, the good news is that given the increase in the number of people who find themselves in the caregiving role and what we now understand about the issues that caregivers face, there are now many sources of support and resources that can help you.

One particular issue many parents are concerned about is the impact their partner's depression is having on their children. There is very little available that addresses this specific issue. It is further complicated by the different considerations required for, say, a three-year-old or a 16-year-old. We have been able to identify some excellent material that addresses this issue, which is included towards the end of this chapter.

We are fortunate to live in an age where not only has our understanding of depression – and mental illness in general – increased by leaps and bounds; but the knowledge and resources that can help us are relatively easy to find, literally in many cases at the tips of our fingers on our computer keyboard.

It might be helpful to start our discussion about the options that are available to you as a caregiver by thinking about three categories of actions you can take to make sure you get the support you need in order to stay whole and healthy:

1. put yourself first

2. get organised, and

3. create a support network.

Put yourself first

I know this seems counterintuitive to many of you. But it goes back to the aircraft safety-briefing flight attendants give passengers before take-off: you need to put your *own* oxygen mask on before helping children with their masks. It's the same concept with caregiving. If you are going to be a carer, you have to learn how to look after yourself.

We know that many of the psychological and health issues that caregivers encounter stem from the fact that they tend not to take care of themselves. So if you find yourself in the role of caregiver, this must become a priority for you.

If you are the type of person who had good boundaries and took care of yourself before your friend or family member became depressed, it might just be a matter of reminding yourself to check in and see how things are going for you. Your routine will undoubtedly change, but it is vitally important to continue to schedule and practise those events and habits that give you a feeling of wellbeing and wholeness.

If you are not that type of person, you may find yourself in the position of learning how to establish boundaries and improve your self-care *at the same time* as you are supporting your depressed loved one. I would encourage you to get help and support in order to do this.

Coping with new emotions

Caregiving can trigger a variety of emotions, some of which may feel uncomfortable. You may feel sad that your friend or family member is struggling with depression. The changes you observe in them as well as the changes in your relationship with them may trigger feelings of grief for having lost 'how things used to be'.

Caregivers often report feeling fearful and anxious: how long will this last? Are they getting better? How can I tell? Is the depression going to make them start acting *really* crazy? And what if they try to kill themselves?

The unknown is always a bit scary, and there are many unknowns when dealing with the course of depression and recovery. It is easy to see how these feelings would surface. When someone we love is suffering, it's a normal reaction for us to feel sadness, grief, fear and anxiety.

Caregivers also commonly report feeling overwhelmed and isolated. Life for most people is hectic enough, what with balancing their professional and personal lives. Add to that the responsibilities of caregiving and most people find themselves struggling to find enough hours in the day to do it all.

Being successful at caregiving too often means giving up any notion of self-care for the caregiver. 'I feel like I've lost myself' is a common theme among caregivers.

There is a whole other set of 'negative' emotions that are also quite common for caregivers to experience. These are not so intuitive at first glance. As caregivers, we might even find ourselves surprised to be feeling these emotions at all. Many caregivers confess that they are a little uncomfortable to discover that they are in fact feeling these types of emotions at all, that's if they're even willing to admit to having them!

For example, have you ever felt *embarrassed* by your friend or family member's depression? The depressed loved one may have held a high-status job or prominent place in the community. Nowadays it isn't just that they can't hold that job or fulfill the role: they might not even be able to get out of bed in the morning. How do you explain that to the neighbours? The situation might have forced the caregiver to take a low-level job (or get a second job in addition to the one they already had), or to get government assistance in order to feed their family because their depressed loved one is incapacitated. In a situation like this, it is not usual for a caregiver to experience feelings of embarrassment and even shame.

And then there's anger. Many caregivers report that dealing with anger is a big challenge for them, especially if they find themselves in the caregiver's role due to familial or other obligations rather than taking on the role by choice.

And of course, let us not forget guilt. Somehow, we tend not to connect the dots between the fact that while we can provide care, we can't wave a magic wand and make our friend or family member all better. We may have superhuman expectations of ourselves that no one on the planet would realistically be able to meet. And so ... we feel guilty.

What can I do about these feelings?

First of all, try not to deny your feelings. See if you can stay in touch with how you are feeling: take a deep breath and check in with yourself. If you don't feel any emotions that you can identify, try a simple body scan.

THE BODY SCAN

Close your eyes, breathe slowly and deeply and focus your attention on your feet and legs, then your lower abdomen, your solar plexus, your chest (near your heart), your arms, your throat, your face and finally the top of your head.

Do you detect any tension or physical sensation in any of those areas? For example, how are you holding your shoulders – up around your ears? That's tension.

If you find areas of tension as you do your scan, stop for a moment and take a deep breath – and then release it.

As you release your breath, imagine that you are releasing the tension at the same time. Sometimes emotion shows up as tension, pain, or some other physical sensation in our body. As you release the tension or bring awareness to the physical sensation, you create a space for the emotion to express itself. You may well feel it bubbling to the surface. Check in to see if an emotion – and which one – comes up for you when you do this exercise.

Depending on our culture and background, we may be more or less comfortable acknowledging emotions. If you were raised in a family where you were chastised for expressing emotion and rewarded for being stoic, being in touch with what you are feeling may not come as naturally to you as it would for someone raised differently. If you find yourself struggling to identify what you are feeling or suspect that you aren't feeling much at all, you might wish to explore ways to improve what psychologists call your 'emotional intelligence'.

Emotional intelligence is 'a different way of being smart. It includes knowing your feelings and using them to make good decisions; managing your feelings well; motivating yourself with zeal and persistence; maintaining hope in the face of frustration; exhibiting empathy and compassion; interacting smoothly; and managing your relationships effectively.[14] Helpguide.org offers a brief questionnaire to help you asses your emotional intelligence.[15]

1. **Are you tolerant of experiencing feelings** that include anger, sadness, fear, disgust, and joy?

2. **Do you experience emotions as** *physical sensations* – in your stomach, chest, shoulders, or elsewhere?

3. **Do your feelings flow freely during the day** – are there times when you're happy and playful; others when you're *sad or mad? Do you find yourself frightened rather than mad* if someone cuts in front of your car?

4. **Are you able to experience intense feelings,** or do you try to numb them? Do you *alter your feelings* into more *acceptable* emotions?

5. **Do you know how to calm down when you feel overwhelmed?**

6. **Do you use emotional feedback in your decision-making processes?** When something sounds good, but feels bad, do you give it a second thought?

7. **Are you comfortable talking about your emotions?**

8. **Do your emotions help you communicate more effectively?**

If you answered most of these questions in the affirmative, chances are you are in touch with your emotions. If not, this is an area you may wish to explore.

Support for you

Make sure you have a support network in place to help you navigate strong emotions. This could range from informal support such as friends and family to a formal network such as a support group or counselling professional. Talking to others about the sadness or grief you may be feeling is very healing. By the same token, talking to people who have been through what you are experiencing can help alleviate feelings of embarrassment: you may discover you are not the only person in the world whose partner is spending the better part of each day in his or her pyjamas at the moment.

A support group can also help you deal with guilt by giving you a reality check. We tend to want to be superhuman and fix everything. As a caregiver, there is always more stuff that we could find to do, and that we feel guilty about if we don't. A support group can help you figure out what is enough and how to forgive yourself – and your depressed friend or family member – when you discover that you don't have superpowers.

Try to remain flexible. We are bombarded daily with media images of perfect people in perfect relationships. Even though intellectually we know that this isn't real, for some reason many of us experience a *disconnect* between our head and our hearts around this. So if our dad isn't perfect or our partner is too depressed to feel romantic, we may feel disappointed. Try to remind yourself that your goal is not to live up to the false standard presented by the media.

Having a friend or family member who is suffering from depression is probably not what you hoped for in life. But if it is your reality, try to accept things as they are and focus on first, taking care of yourself and second, helping as best you know how with your depressed loved one's recovery.

When I asked people I interviewed for this book what they found most helpful for their own wellbeing, the most popular responses were:

Confiding in a friend/family member	84%
Finding other people to share the load of support so it isn't all on my shoulders	62%
Talking to a psychologist or therapist	57%
Talking to a doctor	51%
Communicating on anonymous online forums such as depressioNet. com.au	25%
Being part of a support group	14%

Get organised

Caregivers report that being organised helps them not only deal with the day-to-day, but also helps them deal with the unexpected. If you find yourself in the role of caregiver and you don't have a reliable method (and one which you will follow reliably) to organise things like going through your mail and not letting piles grow, paying your bills each month, getting to regular medical and dental checks-ups, making sure you get your prescriptions refilled on time, getting your car in for routine service, registering for school and so forth, then it's time to look into this and rectify the situation. Get yourself organised. Because this is such a popular topic these days, there are tons of resources online, in bookstores and in libraries. You can even hire someone to create a system for you if you don't want to do it yourself.

One of the main reasons for getting organised is that you will find it akin to a mental lifesaver if you have a day when everything else seems out of control. (And this is not unusual if you have a friend or family member who is depressed!) You don't need the added chaos of looking around and realising you have stacks of unpaid bills, junk mail covering every surface and something that looks like a biology project growing in your refrigerator. Taking care of business is part of the business of taking care.

Plan for the future

Depression = chaos. You can counter this by going ahead and making plans. Realise that you may have to adjust as you go, but planning for the future can help you take concrete steps to deal with fear and reduce the anxiety you may feel.

For example, if your depressed loved one is your partner, realise that sometimes you may have to attend a social function alone. Don't stop going to everything, as you will start to resent your partner. It is wise to confide in friends and tell them that it may be just you that attends or that you may have to cancel at the last minute if there is a crisis.

Create a support network

Many caregivers ask about the type of support they should look for. It really depends on your personal situation; the simple answer is to look for the type of support that helps you stay whole and healthy.

There are three types of support to consider including in your network:

1. Friends and family

This might be your immediate or extended family and could include people you are close enough to that you consider them family even though there is no blood relationship. It is the *nature* of the relationship that matters in this case. Is this a person you can be honest with, that you feel comfortable being your authentic self around and who you trust not to judge you? Consider them the 'go-to' people in your immediate circle of family and friends. They don't require appointments, you don't have to pay them and they will be there when you need them. Just as it is important for the person suffering from depression to have people like this around them (like you for example), you as a caregiver need this type of support as well.

2. Professionals

Therapists, psychologists or general practitioners fall into this category of support. And no, it is not just your depressed loved one who needs support from the health care profession. Think about the peace of mind you gain if you know that your depressed friend or family member has the right team of health care professionals looking after their recovery. It is equally important that you have a team, too, to make sure you stay whole and healthy and that you are able to weather the pressure of being a caregiver with no negative results.

Sometimes there are advantages in having the same professional help as your loved one, although privacy laws will prevent the mental health professional discussing specifics of their care. However there is often much to be gained by having an independent person dedicated to your wellbeing.

Don't hesitate to make an appointment for yourself with a mental health professional if you are struggling.

It is always wise to jot down a few points before your visit to make sure you cover everything. For example:

- Summarise the situation of providing care for your loved one.

- Explain the impact this is having on you and your family. Be specific in how it is affecting you – eg if it is affecting your sleep, explain exactly how it is varying from your norm.

- Give some thought as to what is the main problem you are

experiencing. It is best to focus on one main problem at a time
– trying to solve everything at once can be too overwhelming.

- Make sure you leave with specific strategies to address the problem and an agreed time to revisit (no longer than two weeks) for a next appointment.

Don't be afraid to be assertive if you need help. If you have trouble getting the help that you need, staff at the Commonwealth Carer Resource Centre may be able to advocate on your behalf. They can be contacted on Freecall 1 800 242 636.

3. Support groups

While the advantage of a support network including family and friends and a qualified health care team are clear to just about everyone, support groups are a different story. The support group model works better for some people than for others. So the first step in deciding whether or not to look for a support group is to decide whether or not this is a model that you feel would work for you.

Carers who have found support groups useful say that groups give them a chance to talk about how they are feeling and to receive validation that they are not alone in their experiences.

Support groups also provide the opportunity to share the positive benefits of caregiving: yes, there *are* benefits to being a carer, and it is important to acknowledge the positive! This is a somewhat unique aspect of groups that might not be available from family or friends or the health care profession. If you decide to explore a group as part of your support network, here are some things to consider:

- **Do you want a group with a general or a specific focus?** Some groups offer their services to all caregivers who are supporting loved ones with mental illness, others focus on more specific areas, for example depression or bipolar disorder. There is no reason you can't be involved with two groups if you find that this meets your needs. Just be cognisant of the time involved and don't set yourself up for failure by over-committing your time.

- **Will the group fit your style?** Are you more likely to benefit from a formal, structured meeting or do you prefer to hang out and chat? Pick a group that follows a format you are likely to feel comfortable with.

- **Longevity and leadership.** Look for a group that has some longevity but is still able to attract new members. Ideally, a group will have a good mix of regulars and newer members. Also, look for a group leader who has been or is a caregiver. This experience gives them the ability to relate emotionally to what the group is expressing. A support group is not the place to be theoretical – it requires someone with experience to lead effectively.

- **Be clear about what you will get out of a support group.** Remember that support groups are not therapy. The purpose of a support group is to help its members deal with issues and concerns related to caregiving. It is annoying and uncomfortable when someone in the group does not get this point and brings up what seem like inappropriate issues given the setting. If you find that you've got more on your mind than you think is appropriate for the group, talk to your health care professional. If you have not yet found a doctor or therapist, you could always ask the group leader for a referral.

How do I find a support group for carers?

There are a surprising number of groups out there but they are often hard to find. Most area health services have mental health departments, and these usually have a list of the groups that are available in that area. Another good source is the state chapters of the Association of Relatives and Friends of the Mentally Ill (ARAFMI) and Carers Australia. DepressioNet also has a group of online volunteers that respond to email requests and are often very good at tracking down resources close to you. See the Resources section for further details.

How do you build up a network around you?

So, how *do* you build up a network around you? The answer is a simple two-step process. I do have to add that while simple, for some of us these might not be the easiest two steps in the world to take.

First, admit that you need help. You can't wave a magic wand and cure your friend or family member of depression. You are not super human. You can't do it all. And the truth is, no one is expecting this of you except maybe yourself. If that is the case, figure out what you need to do in order to be open to and accepting of help.

Second, just ask.

Go ahead.

It is okay to ask for help.

It is healthy to ask for help.

People want to help you.

So, ask.

Children affected by a loved one's depression

In the research undertaken for this book, many carers were concerned about the impact their loved one's depression was having on their children. I know in my own situation that at times my depression severely impacted my ability to love and care for my children. Children can often be very confused by a depressed parent's behaviour and it is essential that they feel supported and loved. Finding time to talk to them and letting them know that you care and will support them is very important.

Make sure you inform their teacher if they have a parent with prolonged depression. The teacher will be much better placed to address issues that may arise if they know the root of the problem.

WHAT SHOULD I TELL CHILDREN?

Children can often sense when something is not right. There have probably been changes to their routine; they could be staying with someone else, or a parent could be behaving very differently. It is advisable to tell them what they need to know, how this will impact on their lives. Try to reach an agreement between the significant adults in their lives on what they should be told. Be general in your information and don't necessarily go into details. It is a good idea to ask them to explain back to you what you have just told them to confirm they understand in plain language what you have shared.

It's important that they know:

- **It's not their fault.** Children often believe that they may have caused this illness and they need to be reassured on this point.

- **The illness is not 'catching'.** They may not bring it up but fear of catching a mental illness can be very real for children. Explain that all the causes aren't understood but that it is definitely not contagious.

- **What will happen next.** This may not be completely clear yet, but explain to them to the best of your understanding who will take care of them and what will happen to the unwell person.

Signs to watch out for

The important thing to realise is that children and young people may express their feelings in a range of ways – often they do not have the words or understanding to be able to express them in ways that adults expect or understand.

Children and young people may express themselves in a number of ways:

- **behaviour** – acting out, acting younger or regressing, being anxious; extreme attempts to seek attention

- **physical signs** – nausea, headaches, stomach aches and sleep disturbances

- **cognitive (thinking)** – attention and concentration problems, being preoccupied or being increasingly absorbed in a fantasy life.

It is difficult to pinpoint any specific behaviour that might be a sign that a child is not coping, as all children experience a range of these behaviours, physical signs, and thoughts.

However, it is important to be alert to a sudden or gradual change that might indicate difficulties in coping.

WHAT TO LOOK FOR

The following are some signs of mental health problems in children, adolescents and young people.

- inability to get along with other children

- marked fall in level of school work

- changes in usual sleeping and eating patterns

- marked weight gain or loss

- reluctance to go to school

- fearfulness

- restlessness, fidgeting and trouble concentrating

- excessive disobedience or aggression

- lack of energy or motivation

- social withdrawal

- crying a lot

- feeling hopeless or worthless, and

- odd ideas or behaviours.

If you are concerned for their safety and wellbeing or if symptoms appear to be lasting more than a few weeks, seek professional help. A good place to start is to ask to speak to the Child and Adolescent Mental Health Service (or equivalent) at your local Area Mental Health Service. Kids Helpline may also give you some guidance – call them on 1800 55 1800.

PRESCHOOL-AGED AND YOUNGER CHILDREN

Security is extremely important for babies and infants. Young children feel safest when they are with a person who is familiar and protective, someone they know cares about them. They will feel more secure with fewer carers. Having too many carers can be confusing and disruptive.

Try to provide simple, truthful explanations about what is happening; especially explain any separations from a parent and when they are likely to be reunited.

Even young children can be told 'Mummy is sick in her feelings'.

If possible establish regular visits during any separation. It is valuable to structure contact through play or enjoyable food so that the child has positive contact with their relative.

Common signs of stress in young children are:

- *becoming clingy, tearful or uncooperative*

- *showing sudden changes in eating and sleeping patterns*

- *tantrums or becoming frustrated for no apparent reason, and*

- *initial rejection of contact with parent who they have been separated from.*

Children are very resilient and periods of separation from parents are not harmful, provided the child is adequately cared for.

PRIMARY SCHOOL CHILDREN

As a child becomes older (five to 12 years) they begin to understand and attempt to make sense of their world. They need clear and accurate statements about what is happening and why. Explanations should be given in a clear and truthful manner. It helps them to understand that some behaviours and feelings are symptoms of depression. Children can have their trust in relationships undermined if they feel misled. Withholding facts can make them worry but they should also not be flooded with all the information necessary for an adult. Simple explanations such as the following are appropriate.

> *Daddy has an illness called depression which makes him very sad and sometimes angry. He doesn't mean to shout at you all the time and does not mean to make you feel scared or sad. You did not cause him to get this illness and you can't catch it from him. It will take a while but he will get better. He still loves you very much.*

Some children prefer to be open with peers and some will prefer privacy. It is useful to review with your child what to say to other people, and to explain the reasons why someone should or should not be told. Children often do not know what to say, so it is very helpful for an adult to rehearse this with them.

Some children will attempt to respond to a crisis by becoming a caregiver themselves. They may need guidelines as to which are appropriate responsibilities and roles for them to assume.

ADOLESCENTS

Adolescence is a time of preparation for adult life. Teenagers are practising skills in developing their own identity and are in the process of separating from their family. Friends, instead of family, become the dominant role model for behaviour and expectations.

Adolescents need support and encouragement in gradually separating from their family to accept adult roles. Severe illness in the family can disrupt this process and become a source of conflicting feelings. It helps adolescents if reassurance is given that adequate care is being taken of the ill person.

The adolescent may need to prioritise social contact over family involvement. This process can be complicated and a source of intense conflict if the adolescent feels their practical and emotional support is needed by the family.

Adolescents need concise and factual information about the illness and recovery process. They will also be alert to any implications of a severe illness in the family for their own development. This includes worrying about the possibility that they could develop or show signs of the illness themselves.

Ensure a trustworthy adult is available with whom the adolescent can discuss important practical issues and emotional decisions, such as relationship issues and school or career choices. Adolescents may respond positively to a brief but meaningful exchange when they are feeling relaxed and rapport is good, rather than being sat down for a lengthy 'talking to' or 'lecture'.

Adolescence is also a time when young people experiment with different styles of behaviour as they look for ways to express themselves. Under stress this experimentation may be more extreme. Adolescents may react to stressful situations in many different ways. They may become out of control, withdrawn, moody, confrontational or develop 'hang ups' or start to use drugs or alcohol at risky levels.

Adolescents are also keen observers. Give them the opportunity to express their observations of the ill family member and the impact of the illness on the family. Try to assure them that there are people both within and outside the family that they can talk to about their observations and the impact the illness is having on them personally.

This material is adapted with permission from NSW Health, 'Support for Carers, Family, and Friends – Uncharted Waters', Northern Sydney Central Coast Health Promotion, First edition, 2006.

Step 6: Taking Care of You

'Unfortun[ately] people in [...] wait until t[hey are] experiencing [...] of depression[...] anything[...]

tely, many
arer roles
ey are fully
he symptoms
before doing
about it.'

IT GOES WITHOUT saying that being a caregiver of a depressed loved one can present significant emotional, mental, physical and spiritual challenges. When I spoke to people during the course of working on this book, 59 per cent of respondents said that both their mental and physical health had been adversely affected, and 20 per cent felt that their mental health had been affected.

Mental health

Depression among caregivers is a much-discussed topic. While it is true that many caregivers *do* become depressed, caregiving *does not cause* depression, and not everyone in the caregiver role will experience depression.

Caregiver depression seems to be related to the chronic, long-term stress involved in providing care for the depressed loved one while at the same time keeping everything else going. Caregivers may take on the responsibility of being the family breadwinner or try to fulfill the role of being both father and mother. Children who have a parent suffering from depression may find themselves taking care of their depressed parent instead of the other way around.

The cycle of stress, anger, grief and guilt about these feelings coupled with the physical demands of caregiving – carrying the extra load – can lead caregivers to ignore or even knowingly sacrifice their own emotional, mental, physical and spiritual needs.

Unfortunately, many people in carer roles wait until they are fully experiencing the symptoms of depression before doing anything about it. If you find yourself providing care for a depressed loved one, it's best to start taking steps early on that will help keep you healthy and depression-free.

How will you know if you are in danger of slipping into depression? Again, one of the best things you can do is to stay in touch with what you are feeling. It is not unusual for caregivers to experience feelings of anger, to feel tired or to find themselves overly sensitive or reactive (crying easily, for example). If you find that these feelings become more intense or persist for several weeks, this might be a warning sign of depression.

However, there are many things you can do early on to help mitigate the risk of getting depressed. Exercising regularly, eating a healthy diet, building a robust support network and touching base with a health care professional are all actions you can take *now* to nurture yourself, protect your health and be surrounded by reliable sources of help in the event that you do begin to experience depressive symptoms.

If you suspect you are already starting to feel symptoms of depression yourself, absolutely create an action plan to incorporate these activities into your life.

The following recommendations are from the US National Institute of Mental Health. They are focused on helping caregivers with depression. If they look familiar, that is because, well, they are! It is the same advice you may have shared with your depressed friend or family member for their own benefit.

- Set realistic goals in light of the depression and assume a reasonable amount of responsibility.

- Break large tasks into small ones, set some priorities, and do what you can as you can.

- Try to be with other people and to confide in someone; it is usually better than being alone and secretive.

- Participate in activities that may make you feel better, such as mild exercise, going to a movie or sporting event, or attending a religious, social or community function.

- Expect your mood to improve gradually, not immediately. Feeling better takes time.

- It is advisable to postpone important decisions until the depression has lifted. Before deciding to make a significant transition – change jobs, get married or divorced – discuss it with others who know you well and have a more objective view of your situation.

- People rarely 'snap out of' a depression. But they can feel a little better day by day.

- Remember, positive thinking will replace the negative thinking that is part of the depression. The negative thinking will be reduced as your depression responds to treatment.

- Let your family and friends help you.[16]

STRATEGIES FOR SUSTAINING YOUR WELLBEING

People I interviewed for this book found the following helpful for their own wellbeing:

Having 'me time' for hobbies, movies, friends	88%
Staying healthy myself (exercise, relaxation)	85%

Doing things that improve your physical health are essential, as is the need for 'me' time.

Physical health

The most important aspect of maintaining your physical health as a caregiver is to make sure you are not the only person that your friend or family member can go to for help. We mentioned that carers often neglect their own needs in their desire to help their depressed loved one recover. It goes without saying that if your basic needs are unmet, you are placing yourself at risk of developing health problems. And if you get sick, how are you going to help your depressed friend or family member?

It is very important for both your physical and mental health that you have regular exercise. You should be striving for a 30-minute walk each day. If you are unable to allocate that chunk of time, having two 15-minute walks per day is almost as beneficial. You may even be able to take some of those walks with your loved one and serve two purposes.

Eating well is also an essential part of good health and a diet that is high in fruit, vegetables, and low in fat contributes to wellbeing. See the 'Nutrition' section on page 112 for more information about eating well.

In addition to making sure that you have a good network of support, one of the best things you can do is to make sure that your depressed loved one also has a care network. It is not healthy for either of you to be the only one you have to confide in.

'Me' time

You will see from the carer research above that 'me' time was the most important element in improving their wellbeing.

Take breaks. You need to plan for times when you can get away from the situation. Spend time on your own and do things that nurture you. Giving yourself this space is a great way to keep from getting angry – anger is never a productive emotion – as well as to help you avoid feeling overwhelmed.

Make sure you don't let your caring interfere with the things that bring you pleasure, be that friends, gardening, pets, movies, theatre, shopping, reading, nature, music, massage etc.

Meditation and relaxation

To manage the frantic pace of modern life it is imperative to take time out and still the mind. This can sometimes seem very difficult when the mind is swamped with the negative thoughts that accompany depression. The art of relaxation doesn't happen overnight, but like most things improves with regular practice. See the section on meditation and relaxation on page 111 for more details.

Spirituality

Spirituality means different things to different people. Dealing with a prolonged crisis such as having a loved one suffering from depression can affect the caregiver's beliefs in different ways.

Carers who did not have a strong spiritual foundation before helping their loved one face the challenge of depression may find themselves exploring spiritual support or reconnecting with the religion they grew up with.

Caregivers with strong spiritual foundations may find themselves seeking a deeper connection to support them through the tough times. Conversely, carers may feel temporarily (or permanently) alienated from their spiritual beliefs – angered that this unfair, unpleasant turn of events (having a depressed friend or family member) has landed in their lap.

Part of our nature as human beings is to try and make sense of the things we observe or experience. If you find yourself in the role of caregiver, you will inevitably find yourself asking, 'Why?' We want to know *why* our loved one became depressed, *when* they are going to get well, and *why us*?

There are no answers to these questions. The more energy you spend trying to find an answer, the less energy you will have to devote to other, more productive thought patterns. It's much better to focus your thought energy on finding the ability to accept the situation, on dealing with what is going on, and on being able to recognise that you will grow as a person and possibly learn from even something as disheartening as having a friend or family member afflicted with depression.

What meaning can you find? Seeking meaning in life does not depend on whether or not you believe in God, Buddha, Mohammed or whoever. Ask yourself instead, what does this situation offer you in terms of learning about life and developing as a person? Adversity often provides the opportunity for a transformation of both you and your relationship with a loved one.

Keeping a positive outlook

There is something to be said for being positive. That being said, I realise that there are days (and weeks) when this is a huge challenge for carers. You may feel like you are at the bottom of a well and there is nothing that can raise you out of it. But there are things you can think about to help turn it around:

- Think about the things of a positive nature that have come out of being a caregiver, for example the ways that caregiving has made you a stronger person.

- Think about what motivated you to take on the role of the caregiver in the first place.

- Has your role as a caregiver allowed you to get closer to your friend or family member?

- What are the things you most like about your friend or family member? Can you view your caregiving as part of the process to help them be able to express those characteristics once again?

Living in the present

Many of the people I interviewed for this book stressed how worrying it is caring for a loved one with depression. They often feel consumed by the chronic nature of the illness and start to believe that things will never get better. Those who are able to look back with the benefit of hindsight, however, highlight how important it is to take the journey one day at a time. Much grief is caused by dreading the future or agonising over what might have been. For an excellent perspective on this, Eckhart Tolle's book, *The Power of Now,* is a great resource.

Wisdom from fellow travellers

In the research for this book, we asked people that had been caring for someone with depression what they knew now that they wished they'd known when they started this journey. We asked for open-ended responses and then endeavoured to categorise them to see what was most frequently listed. They were as follows:

1. Get them to a GOOD doctor for an accurate diagnosis earlier.

2. Be patient – things do improve. It is not always smooth sailing and you have to expect the ups with the downs.

3. It's not my fault that they are depressed.

4. I have to look after my own wellbeing otherwise I'm no good to anyone.

5. They have to take responsibility for their own recovery. I can't do it for them.

6. You need to understand how to navigate around the mental health system.

7. It affects EVERYTHING if you let it.

Below are a selection of those responses.

> *Nothing I say can change the situation. I can't fix him. All I can do is offer support and love.*
>
> *It won't get any better by itself – ongoing professional treatment is needed to make a difference.*
>
> *I wish I had recognised the symptoms as his depression rather than thinking we only had marriage problems.*

I should have availed myself of some of the support offered by friends and family.

I am not responsible for making them better but can only be there to love and support them.

It's a strain for the whole family. A constant rollercoaster.

I wished I understood that he was mentally ill and not a bastard.

It is important not to become a 'doormat' and be afraid of their strong emotions.

I [felt I] was not getting a partner but a child.

I wish I had recognised that he needed help earlier and just how damaged he was.

Medication is not the only answer.

Depressed people are selfish [but you can't] take it personally.

I learned to tell doctors it's worse than it was just so we could get help now not next week.

Getting a PROPER early diagnosis is paramount.

How to navigate the mental health maze. Keep looking for a GP until you find one that knows their way around.

That they would recover and become the person that they used to be again.

How to let go.

My children were more at risk of suffering depression because my wife suffers from the disorder.

It doesn't last forever and it doesn't always worsen.

I am much more emotionally detached from the issues than I was earlier on – learning how to do that has been a challenge. Also, [I learnt] that it's okay to feel angry at someone for not wanting to help themselves and causing everyone around them a lot of stress and trouble.

That it won't go away overnight.

Don't take it personally! They still love you even when they snap at you.

I would take action about the situation a lot sooner.

That she will come back to normal and that she really does love life and her family.

That there is more help out there and not to wait, organise help early yourself.

Most of my useful discoveries have been in my own personal evolution not in how to label or manage her.

I wish I learnt some of the strategies on how to cope myself earlier rather than becoming absorbed too much with their life.

Be patient and look to the future. Take the bad days with the good. Focus on remembering the good times. Don't focus on the depression.

No one can help them until they decide that they want to be helped.

I wished I'd linked [both of us up] with [health care professionals] earlier.

Speak up for myself and keep looking till I find the right support for me.

That I was not to blame even though they tried to tell me I was.

A 'bad day' is not necessarily a setback.

Would've taken them to doctor before it got too bad/suicidal.

I wish I'd not walked on egg shells around him but rather had addressed issues in a more proactive way. It is so much easier now everything is out in the open and we all see it is a condition to be managed, not something to be ashamed of. It is what we do about it that matters.

Sometimes they just need you to listen and be there to hug them.

I can only do what I am capable of doing re support.

I wish I'd been able to recognise the tell-tale signs so I could have helped them earlier.

Mental health problems are very common within the rural male population and a lot of the medicines for depression can make the situation worse or fix one part while creating other negative side-effects.

To protect and look after myself before looking after them.

What to do to avert it in the first place.

That the depressed person you see isn't really the person you love.

The cause.

What a great toll it would take on me and my own family.

Getting them to see a GP sooner rather than later.

That telling them to just get over it doesn't work and is very negative to them.

That with time and cognitive behavioural counselling, there will be light at the end of the tunnel.

It's okay to challenge them. It's okay to be frustrated by the slow progress.

How to fight the system to get help.

There are good days and bad days — enjoy the good days.

That it is about them, not about the relationship.

That it is not my fault and to stop asking the question 'what's wrong?' because they often don't know themselves.

How much it affects EVERYTHING.

That very little can be fixed by the members of the family unit. An outside, objective opinion must be heard.

That with patience, love and medication the problem can be bearable.

That it is the disease talking/behaving. Not the person.

Get medication and a GOOD DOCTOR earlier.

Don't ever think you can manage alone.

There are people who care (but to find them is another thing). ""

'I lea

tell doctors

than it wa

could ge

not nex

ned to

t was worse

just so we

help now

week.'

STOP

Step 7:
Surviving
a Crisis

Step 7: Surviving a Crisis

'There i
that you sh
to someo
depressed a

a myth
ld not talk
e who is
out suicide.'

THE MOST LIKELY crisis that you may face if you are helping care for a depressed friend or family member is self-harm or an attempted or successful suicide. It is a subject that no one – even medical professionals – is at ease talking about. But in the event that you find yourself facing this challenge, two things are important. First, doing what you can to recognise that your depressed loved one is reaching the point of considering suicide as a viable alternative and second, taking appropriate action to prevent it.

Having attempted suicide four times I have quite a deal of first-hand knowledge regarding this subject. I have also spoken to many loved ones of people who have attempted suicide and know how fearful they are of it being repeated. From personal experience and reading research I know that most people with depression don't want to die but are seeking a way to end the pain. I made the last attempt on my life on 24 July 2004 after a horrendous four-year struggle with depression. At that time I was 100 per cent convinced that I would never be normal again. The depressed person's outlook is not rational.

Suicide is especially taboo in Western culture. It carries a painful stigma above and beyond the loss itself.

The US-based Centers for Disease Control (CDC) reports that while most suicide attempts involve chronic mental health problems such as depression, there are also what researchers called 'impulsive suicide attempts' that were immediately preceded by some kind of conflict rather than the person being motivated by an overwhelming desire to die.

'We know a great deal about the underlying conditions that predispose an individual to kill himself – heredity, severe mental illness, an impulsive or violent temperament. We know too that some events or circumstances in life interact in a particularly deadly way with these predisposing vulnerabilities,' says Kay Redfield Jamison, professor of psychiatry at Johns Hopkins University and author of many books, including *Night Falls Fast: Understanding Suicide*.[17]

Depression is considered a strong risk factor for suicide and, in fact, suicidal thoughts and behaviour can be considered symptoms of moderate to severe depression.

Assessing the risk of self-harm

The United States Air Force has an acronym, 'LINK', which they use to offer advice on how to prepare yourself for a crisis. In this case, LINK might stand for:

L – Look for the indicators.

I – Inquire or ask the person about how they are doing, including suicidal thoughts.

N – Note the level of seriousness.

K – Know how to get help.

The threat of suicide is one of those situations that require us to put aside our own feelings of discomfort, the desire for the issue to 'just go away' and our own fears. We have to take action.

Most people experience thoughts of suicide (this is known as *suicidal ideation*) before they actually come up with a plan to attempt it. The actual plan for when, where and how they will suicide is usually something that is developed over time. According to the Mental Health First Aid Training and Research Program (MFHA) at the University of Melbourne, 'a higher level of planning indicates a more serious risk'. They add, however, that the lack of a plan does not ensure that someone is safe from attempting suicide. MFHA suggest three questions to help you determine if your friend or family member has a definite intention to take their life.

1. Have you decided how you would kill yourself?

2. Have you decided when you would do it?

3. Have you taken any steps to secure the things you would need to carry out your plan?

MFHA guidelines also stress the importance of knowing what other risk factors might be involved, including:

- Has the person been using alcohol or other drugs? The use of alcohol and other drugs can make a person more susceptible to acting on impulse.

- Has the person made a suicide attempt in the past? A previous suicide attempt makes a person more likely to make a future suicide attempt or to kill themselves.[18]

Remember that suicide is an ambivalent act – people have both positive and negative feelings about what they are considering. Suicide goes against the grain of our natural instinct to survive. It makes sense that with treatment, most people can let go of the idea of suicide as a viable option for them.

It is not uncommon for people to tell someone before they attempt suicide. There is a myth that you should not talk to someone who is depressed about suicide, that talking about it may somehow introduce the idea to them and motivate the person to kill themselves. This is completely false.

Because depression is one of the risk factors that can contribute to suicidal behaviour, chances are that your depressed friend or family member has already thought about it. Talking about it is healthy and proactive.

You need to know if they have or are considering suicide and you especially need to know if they have formulated a plan. By bringing it up and giving them the chance to talk to you about it, you may actually be helping them to get the help they need in order to prevent a suicide attempt. To give you some ideas about how vulnerable they are, you can ask: 'If you had to rate your mood between 1 and 10, where 1 is actively suicidal and 10 is 100 per cent normal, where would you be?'

Warning signs

There are several indicators that you can look for that may help you figure out if your depressed loved one is suicidal. There are many resources and websites dedicated to this subject, but some of the warning signs include:

- threatening to hurt or kill themselves

- looking for ways to kill themselves: seeking access to pills, weapons or other means

- talking or writing about death, dying or suicide

- expressing feelings of hopelessness

- exhibiting rage or anger; seeking revenge

- acting recklessly or engaging in risky activities, seemingly without thinking

- feeling trapped, acting as if there's no way out

- increasing alcohol or drug use

- withdrawing from friends, family or society

- experiencing anxiety, agitation, being unable to sleep or sleeping all the time

- having dramatic changes in mood, and

- not seeing any reason for living, no sense of purpose in life.[19]

What can you do?

If someone tells you they are thinking about suicide, don't judge them; listen and take them seriously. Talking to them directly is one of the most powerful things you can do to help them change their state of mind. Remember that you are not trying to talk them out of the bad feelings they might be having, just to consider options other than suicide. Ask them if they have a plan.

Don't be afraid to express your concern. This is different than being judgmental ('you shouldn't be having those thoughts') or minimising a person's feelings ('it's not *that* bad; there are lots of people who are much worse off').

If your depressed friend or family member tells you that they are thinking of suicide, strongly encourage them to talk to a professional. Follow up with them *and* their health care professional if you are legally able to do so given your relationship. Under no circumstances should you keep a discussion about suicidal thoughts a secret even if your friend or family member asks you to. Talk to the person and come up with a plan for keeping them safe over the next few hours or days. This might include you reaching out to health care professionals or suicide support groups on their behalf. Offer to go with the person to get help.

If you sense that the person is in immediate danger of harming himself or herself, do not leave them alone. Dial the Suicide Callback Service on 1300 659 467 (or 911 for emergency services in the US) and get help.

Aftermath of a suicide attempt

There is no fail-safe way to predict whether or not a person will attempt to commit suicide. If your depressed loved one tries to take their life and you are present, remember that the first priority is getting medical help immediately. Focus on staying centred and being reassuring. Once the person is no longer in imminent physical danger, make sure that you stay in close contact with them.

If they do not have a support network, take steps to put this in place. Remember that you want to include friends and family, health care professionals and support groups (as appropriate) in this network. A depressed person who has attempted suicide is now dealing with two intense stigmas: suffering from a mental illness and having attempted suicide. Now more than ever they need to feel loved, supported and accepted.

The aftermath of a suicide attempt is also a time for you as a caregiver to tap into your own support network. Inevitably, you will replay all the previous conversations and actions with your depressed loved one to see if you can identify *anything* you could have done differently in order to prevent their suicide attempt. You may find that you are experiencing guilt and shame. I can tell you here in this book and you can read in the many other resources available that there is nothing you could have done. *Understanding* this fact intellectually will not alleviate these feelings. You need to process this intense experience and it is in your best interests to seek help in doing so.

How you can give hope

As I explained before, the suicidal mind is usually not rational. Intellectually they understand that many other people get over depression, but they often reason, 'They obviously weren't as bad as I am'. When I was feeling really suicidal I yearned for stories of people who had overcome depression. That was the motivation for writing *Back from the Brink*. I would encourage your depressed loved one to read the stories of Brian Egan, Kathy McMahon, and Sonia Attard from *Back from the Brink*. These people all believed their situation was hopeless but went on to overcome the most terrible obstacles and eventually recover and give hope to others. I personally know that it is possible to believe with 100 per cent certainty that you can't get better and yet go on to lead an incredibly fulfilling life.

Contact numbers to keep at hand

For your own peace of mind I suggest you keep the following numbers close at hand. You can't predict when a crisis might happen and it is best to be prepared.

- Their GP

- Their psychiatrist

- Their psychologist

- Your local area 24/7 mental health support line

- Accident and Emergency at your local hospital

- Lifeline 13 11 14

- Mensline 1300 789 978

- Kids Helpline 1800 551 800

- Suicide Callback Service 1300 659 467

Suicide callback service

The Suicide Callback service is a free nationwide telephone support service for those displaying suicidal behaviour, for carers for those at risk, and for those bereaved by suicide. It supports callers through a series of up to six 50-minute telephone counselling sessions, scheduled to suit the caller. The service operates seven days a week from 10am to 8.30pm and is staffed by professional counselors, with specialist skills in working with suicide-related issues. It can serve as an excellent bridge before your loved one is able to have face-to-face counselling. It can also serve as a wonderful resource for you.

AUSTRALIA-BASED ONLINE RESOURCES

- Suicide Helpline (www.suicidehelpline.org.au)

- Suicide Prevention Australia (www.suicidepreventionaust.org)

- Lifeline (www.lifeline.org.au)

- LIFE (www.livingisforeveryone.com.au)

US-BASED ONLINE RESOURCES

- Suicide Prevention Resource Center (www.sprc.org)

- National Institute of Mental Health (www.nimh.nih.gov)

- National Strategy for Suicide Prevention (www.mentalhealth. samhsa.gov/suicideprevention/default.asp)

- American Association of Suicidology (www.suicidology.org/)

- Suicide Awareness Voices of Education (www.save.org/)

- Suicide Prevention Action Network USA (www.spanusa.org/)

- American Foundation for Suicide Prevention (www.afsp.org/)

- Mayo Clinic (www.mayoclinic.com/health/suicide/MH00048)

- Substance Abuse and Mental Health Services Administration (www.samhsa.gov)

- National Suicide Prevention Lifeline 1 800 273 TALK (1 800 273 8255)

Resources & References

Resources & References

USEFUL RESOURCES

- The Black Dog Institute's online self-testing assessment for depression: www.blackdoginstitute.org.au/public/depression/howtotell/selftesting.cfm

- Graeme Cowan's first book, Back from the Brink, and related online resources: www.IamBackFromTheBrink.com

- For help in choosing a therapist, go to www.goodtherapy.com.au, which provides information and advice about finding a therapist to suit you or your loved one.

- Information about the different depression medications and their contraindications can be found on beyondblue's website: www.beyondblue.org.au/index.aspx?link_id=7.981

KEY CONTACTS

- Ambulance 000

- ARAFMI
    Northern Territory 08 8948 1051
    NSW City 02 9332 0700
    NSW Country 1800 655 198
    Queensland 07 3254 1881
    South Australia 08 8221 5166
    Tasmania 03 6224 7247
    Victoria 03 9889 3733
    Western Australia 08 9228 0577

- beyondblue info line 1300 224 636

- Carers Australia   02 6122 9900
    NSW   02 9280 4744
    VIC   03 9396 9500
    QLD   07 3843 1401
    SA   08 8271 6288
    WA   08 9444 5922
    TAS   03 6231 5507
    ACT   02 6296 9900
    NT   08 8948 4877

- Commonwealth Carelink Centre 1800 052 222
  Single point of contact for community care services

- Commonwealth Carer Respite Centres 1800 059 059

- Commonwealth Carer Resource Centre 1800 242 636

- GROW   1800 558 268

- Gay & Lesbian Counselling Line   1800 184 527

- Kids Helpline   1800 551 800

- Lifeline   13 11 14
  Lifeline Information Service   1300 13 11 14
  (Information – not telephone counselling)

- Mensline   1300 789 978

- Mental Health Information Service   1300 794 991

- NSW Rural Mental Health Support Line   1800 201 123

- Parentline
    NSW   13 20 55
    VIC   13 22 89
    QLD   1300 301 300
    SA   1300 364 100
    WA   1800 654 432
    TAS   1800 808 178
    ACT   02 6287 3833

- Police emergency 000

- Relationships Australia 1300 364 277
  Provides counselling, mediation and post separation
  parenting issues

- SANE helpline 1800 688 382

- Suicide callback service 1300 659 467

- Veterans Line 1800 043 503

- Vietnam Veterans 1800 011 046

AUSTRALIAN ORGANISATIONS AND WEBSITES

- **Anxiety Disorders Alliance**
  www.ada.mentalhealth.asn.au

- **Association of Relatives and Friends of the Mentally Ill (ARAFMI)**
  www.arafmiaustralia.asn.au

- **beyondblue**
  www.beyondblue.org.au

- **Blackdog Institute**
  www.blackdoginstitute.org.au

- **Blue Pages**
  www.bluepages.anu.edu.au
  *Good listing of national and international sites and what works to
  overcome depression*

- **Carers Alliance**
  www.carers.org.au

- **Carers' Australia**
  www.carersaustralia.com.au
  Gives full listing of resources and state associations

- **Carers Network**
  www.carersnetwork.org

- **Carers Support and Respite Centre**
  www.carersupport.org.au

- **COMIC (Children of Mentally Ill Consumers)**
  www.howstat.com/comic
  Good guide for informing and preparing children about a mentally ill parent

- **depressioNet**
  www.depressioNet.com.au

- **Good Therapy**
  www.goodtherapy.com.au
  To assist in finding a therapist in your area

- **GROW**
  www.grow.net.au
  12 Step mental health support groups

- **Kid's Helpline**
  www.kidshelp.com.au

- **Lifeline**
  www.lifeline.org.au

- **Lifeline's Justask**
  www.justask.org.au
  Lifeline's rural mental health support line

- **Lifeline's Justlook**
  www.justlook.org.au
  Lifeline's database of low cost (or free) health and community services

- **Mensline Australia**
  www.menslineaus.org.au

- **Mental Health Association NSW**
  www.mentalhealth.asn.au

- **MoodGYM**
  www.moodgym.anu.edu.au
  A free online cognitive behaviour therapy program developed by the Australian National University

- **PADA**
  www.panicanxietydisorder.org.au

- **PANDA**
  www.panda.org.au
  For those with post or antenatal depression

- **Reachout**
  www.reachout.asn.au
  For young people with depression

- **SANE**
  www.sane.org

- **Young Carers**
  www.youngcarersnsw.asn.au

OVERSEAS WEBSITES

Carer

- **Action for Carers and Employment**
  www.acecarers.org.uk

- **Caregiver's Home Companion**
  www.caregivershome.com

- **Carers UK**
  www.carersuk.org

- **The Princess Royal Trust for Carers**
  www.carers.org

- **Family Caregiver Alliance**
  www.caregiver.org

- **National Family Caregivers Association**
  www.nfcacares.org

Depression

- **Bipolar Kids Homepage**
  www.geocities.com/EnchantedForest/1068

- **BPSO-Bipolar Significant Others**
  www.bpso.org

- **Child & Adolescent Bipolar Foundation**
  www.bpkids.org

- **Depression Alliance Online**
  www.depressionalliance.org

- **Depression.com**
  www.depression.com

- **Depression Resource Centre**
  www.healingwell.com/depression

- **Dr. Ivan's Depression Central**
  www.psycom.net/depression.central.html

- **How to Explain Bipolar Disorder to Others**
  www.bipolar.about.com/library/howto/htexplain.htm

- **Internet Mental Health**
  www.mentalhealth.com/p20-grp.html

- **McMan's Depression and Bipolar Web**
  www.mcmanweb.com

- **Mental Health Foundation**
  www.mentalhealth.org.uk

- **National Depressive and Manic-Depressive Association**
  www.ndmda.org

- **National Institute of Mental Health**
  www.nimh.nih.gov

- **Paediatric Psychiatry by Jim Chandler MD**
  http://jamesdauntchandler.tripod.com/table_of_contents

- **Pendulum Resources**
  www.pendulum.org

- **Postpartum Depression**
  http://postpartum.net

- **Psychology Information Online**
  www.psychologyinfo.com

- **Wing of Madness: A Depression Guide**
  www.wingofmadness.com

SUGGESTED READING

Carer

Beardslee, William R, *When a Parent is Depressed*

Carter, Rosalyn and Golanf, Susan, *Helping Someone with Mental Illness*

Johnstone, Mathew, *Living With a Black Dog*

Rosen, Laura and Amador, Xavier, *When Someone You Love is Depressed*

Sheffield, Anne, *How You Can Survive When They're Depressed*

General depression

Greenberger, Dennis and Padesky, Christine A., *Mind over Mood: Change How You Feel by Changing the Way You Think*

Johnstone, Matthew, *I Had a Black Dog*

Parker, Gordon, *Dealing with Depression: A Commonsense Guide to Mood Disorders, second edition*

Solomon, Andrew, *Noonday Demon: An Atlas of Depression*

Tanner, Susan and Ball, Jillian, *Beating the Blues: A Self-Help Approach to Overcoming Depression*

Firsthand accounts

Cowan, Graeme, *Back From the Brink: Australians Tell Their Stories of Overcoming Depression*

Manning, Martha, *Undercurrents: A Therapist's Reckoning with Her Own Depression*

Styron, William, *Darkness Visible: A Memoir of Madness*

Thompson, Tracy, *The Beast: A Journey Through Depression*

Wigney, Tessa, Eyers, Kerrie, and Parker, Gordon, *Journeys with the Black Dog: Inspirational Stories of Bringing Depression to Heel*

Bipolar disorder

Goodwin, Frederick K. and Jamison, Kay Redfield, *Manic-Depressive Illness: Bipolar Disorders and Recurrent Depression*

Jamison, Kay Redfield, *Touched With Fire: Manic-Depressive Illness and the Artistic Temperament*

Miklowitz, David J., *The Bipolar Disorder Survival Guide: What You and Your Family Need to Know*

Mondimore, Francis Mark, *Bipolar Disorder: A Guide for Patients and Families*

Torrey, E. Fuller, and Knable, Michael B., *Surviving Manic Depression: A Manual on Bipolar Disorder for Patients, Families, and Providers*

Firsthand accounts

Cheney, Terri, *Manic: A Memoir*

Jamison, Kay Redfield, *An Unquiet Mind*

Rowe, Penelope and Rowe, Jessica, *The Best of Times, the Worst of Times: Our Family's Journey with Bipolar*

Childhood depression

Cytryn, Leon and McKnew, Donald, *Growing Up Sad: Childhood Depression and its Treatment*

Papolos, Demitri and Papolos, Janice, *The Bipolar Child: The Definitive and Reassuring Guide to Childhood's Most Misunderstood Disorder*

Adolescent depression

Koplewicz, Harold S., *More Than Moody*

Mondimore, Francis Mark, *Adolescent Depression*

Firsthand accounts

Irwin, Cait and Evans, Dwight L. and Wasmer Andrews, Linda, *Monochrome Days: A firsthand account of one teenager's experience with depression*

Jamieson, Patrick E. and Rynn, Moira A,. *Mind Race: A Firsthand Account of One Teenager's Experience with Bipolar Disorder (Adolescent Mental Health Initiative)*

Post-natal depression

Firsthand accounts

Shaw, Fiona, *Composing Myself: A Journey Through Postpartum Depression*

Shields, Brooke, *Down Came The Rain: My Journey Through Postpartum Depression*

Anxiety disorders

Bourne, Edmund J., *The Anxiety & Phobia Workbook, Fourth Edition*

Steketee, Gail and White, Kerrin, *When Once is Not Enough: Help for Obsessive-Compulsives*

Firsthand accounts

Bell, Jeff, *Rewind, Replay, Repeat: A Memoir of Obsessive-Compulsive Disorder*

Ford, Emily, Liebowitz, Michael and Wasmer Andrews, Linda: *What You Must Think of Me: A Firsthand Account of One Teenager's Experience with Social Anxiety Disorder (Adolescent Mental Health Initiative)*

Kant, Jared, Franklin, Martin and Wasmer Andrews ,Linda, *The Thought That Counts: A Firsthand Account of One Teenager's Experience with Obsessive-Compulsive Disorder (Adolescent Mental Health Initiative)*

General mental health and self help

Bloch, Sidney and Singh, Bruce S, *Understanding Troubled Minds: A Guide to Mental Illness and its Treatment*

Butler-Bowdon, Tom, *50 Psychology Classics*

Butler-Bowdon, Tom, *50 Self-Help Classics*

Jamison, Kay Redfield, *Night Falls Fast: Understanding Suicide*

Norcross, John, C et al, *Authoritative Guide to Self-Help Resources in Mental Health*

Seligman, Martin, *Authentic Happiness*

Seligman, Martin, *Learned Optimism*

Christian

Lockley, John, *A Practical Workbook for the Depressed Christian*

Stone, Howard W., *Depression and Hope: New Insights for Pastoral Counselling*

Williams, Chris, Richards, Paul and Whitton, Ingrid, *I'm Not Supposed to Feel Like This: A Christian Self-Help Approach to Depression and Anxiety*

ARAFEMI

ARAFEMI Victoria has a range of support services for people with mental illness and their families. There is a strong focus on peer support for both carers and people with depression, with regular groups being held. Staff advocate a recovery orientated approach, and there are many examples of how people have reached new levels of daily community living they had previously lost. In many, if not most, families and carers play an active and persistent role. ARAFEMI provides a Telephone Helpline, referral and information services, as well as education sessions and support groups. Over 90 people with a mental illness are supported to live in community or state funded housing.

ARAFEMI works closely with clinical providers, a good example being the Linwood Prevention and Recovery Service where 'step-up and step-down' strategies are used to assist people in crisis.

Carer Helpline 03 9810 9314 or visit www.arafemi.org.au

For contact details of other state offices visit www.arafmiaustralia.asn.au and see 'Member Organisations'.

beyondblue: the national depression initiative

beyondblue is a national, independent, not-for-profit organisation working to address issues associated with depression, anxiety and related substance use disorders in Australia.

beyondblue is a bipartisan initiative of the Australian, State and Territory Governments. Its key goals are raising community awareness about depression and reducing stigma associated with the illness.

beyondblue works in partnership with health services, schools, workplaces, universities, media and community organisations, as well as people living with depression, to bring together their expertise.

For information on depression, available treatments and where to get help, visit www.beyondblue.org.au or call the beyondblue info line on 1300 22 4636.

beyondblue: opening our eyes to depression across Australia

BLACK DOG INSTITUTE

The Black Dog Institute is a clinical research, education and community support facility focusing on both depression and bipolar disorder.

Our research team focuses on causes and treatments, with treatment studies ranging across drugs, transcranial magnetic stimulation, fish oil and acupuncture. Its clinics provide comprehensive assessments and management strategies for people referred by general practitioners or psychiatrists. Professional educational programs are provided to psychiatrists, general practitioners, psychologists, school counsellors and workforce administrators. The two-storey Institute, based at the Prince of Wales Hospital, has a walk-in community centre providing information to those with a mood disorder (and their families), support group counselling and reference books. The team also provides talks to organisations around New South Wales and ensures a practical and informative website. The overall message of the Institute is that there are multiple differing mood disorders which require and benefit from sophisticated assessment and management.

www.blackdoginstitute.org.au

Carers NSW is the peak organisation in the state for relatives and friends who care for people with a disability, mental health problem, chronic condition, terminal illness or who are frail aged.

Membership for carers and carer support groups is free and our services for carers include:

- information and publications

- emotional support and referral to counselling

- education and training,

A range of specific carer support programs including the Family and Carer Mental Health Program that offers dedicated support to carers of people with a mental illness.

For more information or to join Carers NSW call 1800 242 636 (free call except from mobiles) or visit www.carersnsw.asn.au

For contact details and websites for all states visit www.carersaustralia.com.au

depressioNet.
com.au

DepressioNet is a unique, Australian not-for-profit organisation that provides comprehensive information, help and peer-based support for people who want to manage their depression. The service is web-based and operates 24 hours per day, seven days per week.

Our purpose is to empower people to make informed choices and find solutions to the challenges of living with depression. depressioNet is created by and for people from a variety of backgrounds who live with depression. The principles on which depressioNet is anchored – self-help, peer support and empowerment – are simple, yet compelling. Our service is practical and highly personalised. The community we serve, those living with depression, their families, friends and colleagues, exist throughout metropolitan, regional and rural Australia.

www.depressioNet.com.au

GROW is a community mental health organisation which began in Sydney in 1957. It has since spread to all Australian states and territories and to the United States, Ireland, New Zealand and Canada. GROW offers an experience based, research validated 12-step program which has come out of the lives of mental health sufferers themselves. It provides a recovery-focused program for adults with mental illness and those seeking prevention of mental illness.

In this 50th anniversary year of GROW's operations, there are approximately 300 groups throughout Australia. In addition, GROW runs a dual-diagnosis (mental illness plus drug addiction) residential rehabilitation program for up to 17 people located at West Hoxton in Sydney, and accommodation support programs in Brisbane and Canberra. GROW receives funding from all State and Territory Governments and can be contacted Australia-wide by telephoning 1800 558 268 or at www.grow.net.au

Mensline Australia is a national service that supports men who are dealing with family and relationship difficulties, particularly those surrounding family breakdown or separation.

We offer anonymous telephone support, information and referral for men around Australia, 24 hours a day, seven days a week, for the cost of a local call. Mensline Australia's counsellors are paid professionals trained to provide counselling responses and approaches that specifically suit the way men think and behave. They also have ready access to relevant information and referral to men's services at any time and from anywhere in the country. Mensline Australia is managed by Crisis Support Services, a not-for-profit, non-government organisation that also operates several other specialist services.

Call Mensline on 1300 78 99 78

The Mensline website www.menslineaus.org.au offers resources for both service users and providers.

AUSTRALIA

The national mental health charity. Working for a better life for people affected by mental illness.

SANE Australia works for a better life for people affected by mental illness through campaigning for improved services and attitudes; educating the community about mental illness and related topics, and researching practical solutions to help improve quality of life.

SANE Helpline: 1800 18 SANE (7263) www.sane.org

Freecall
Call Freecall 1800 18 SANE (7263) from anywhere in Australia for confidential information and advice on mental illness.
Helpline Online: helpline@sane.org or via www.sane.org

Information
SANE publishes easy to understand books, pamphlets and DVDs explaining mental illness and how to help. See the SANE Bookshop www.sane.org

RESOURCES & REFERENCES

Practical Strategies
for Your Peace of Mind

Having chosen to read this book you have demonstrated your care and commitment to helping your loved one. But the truth is, a paperback isn't the best medium to provide all the advice you need. For a start it just isn't big enough. It also doesn't allow you to listen to interviews or view videos.

This workbook will show you how to:

- Tailor questions to understand how they really feel and encourage them to see a doctor or psychologist
- Suggest options if they refuse to see a doctor
- Ensure they have access to the knowledge of the world's best psychiatrists to get the right diagnosis ASAP (even if you live in Burke)
- Access help lines to know where your local resources are
- Follow a simple lifestyle plan to ensure you don't sacrifice your health whilst caring for a loved one
- Prepare a care plan for children affected by their parent's depression

- Minimise the impact of antidepressants on intimacy and sex
- Access a more comprehensive resource listing.

In addition to the workbook, you will receive:

- Recordings of interviews I have had with experts on caring for someone with a mental illness, depression medication, choosing the right psychologist, and relaxation/meditation.

For full details visit:
www.DepressionCarer.com/workbook

Managing Depression in the Workplace

The University of Queensland estimates that depression costs the Australian economy $6 billion per year and yet in research done for 'Back from the Brink' only 9% of people with depression feel comfortable discussing it with work colleagues. (See 'Best Practice in Managing Mental Health in the Workplace' at www.IamBackFromTheBrink. com/work)

Most managers and colleagues are well meaning and supportive but struggle to know how to discuss this illness and how to support the affected person.

This course and accompanying workbook help you to:

- Understand the causes and symptoms of depression and anxiety disorders and how they impact behaviour in the workplace

- Prepare yourself to speak with someone you suspect could be affected

- Suggest strategies that ensure they get the right professional help

- Prepare alternative strategies if they resist acknowledging a problem or seeking help

- Know when and how to tell colleagues in their work group

- Reduce the negative impact that a depressed employee can have on their work group and customers.

- Ensure they get proper integrated care from Employee Assistance Programs, doctors, and psychologists.

- Create a flexible environment that promotes wellbeing and aids recovery.

This problem is too big to ignore. Whilst there are no quick fixes, relief lies in finding practical solutions.

For full details see:
www.WorkDepressionAdvice. com/help

References

1   Sheila M LoboPrabhu, MD, Victor A Molinari, PhD and James W Lomax, MD, **Supporting the Caregiver in Dementia**, JHU Press, 2006, p. 26.

2   Laura Epstein Rosen, PhD and Xavier Francisco Amador, PhD, **When Someone You Love is Depressed**, The Free Press, 1996.

3   Carer quotes in Chapter 1 and 2 come from:Nicole Highet, et al **The experience caring for a person with depression** (2003) beyondblue

     Nicole Highet, et al **How much more do we have to lose? Carer and family perspectives of living with a person with depression** Medical Journal of Australia (2004)

     All other quotes come from research conducted for Back From The Brink Too

4   Oregon Department of Human Services - www.oregon.gov/DHS/spwpd/caregiving/care_caregiver. shtml#selfassess and;

     American Medical Association - www.rcaging.org/opencms/Programs_Services/Family_Caregiver_Support/AMA_assessment_tool.pdf.

5   www.nfcacares.org.

6   Information in this section has come from the following websites: www.mayoclinic.com/health/antidepressants/MH00062;
     www.nimh.nih.gov/health/publications/medications/complete-publication.shtml;
     www.beyondblue.org.au/index.aspx?link_id=7.981&tmp=FileDownload&fid=723.

7   US Preventive Services Task Force, **Screening for depression: recommendations and rationale**, Annals of Internal Medicine, vol. 136, 2002, pp. 760–4.

8   Hara Estroff Marano, **Depression: A Family Matter**, Psychology Today, 2002.

9   The self-test is used with permission.

10   The following material is used with the permission of the Black Dog Institute.

11   Andrea Dunn PhD et al, **Exercise Treatment for Depression: Efficacy and Dose Response**, American Journal of Preventative Medicine, January 2005.

12   Reproduced with permission of the Black Dog Institute.

13   Dr Paul Ekman, a pioneering psychologist in the study of emotions and facial expressions, has written several books on the subject and has authored a one-hour training course, the Micro Expression Training Tool, which is available online (www.mettonline.com).

14   Daniel Goleman, **Emotional Intelligence**, Bantam, 1995.

15   Helpguide.org. Reproduced with permission.

16   Reproduced with permission of the US National Institute of Mental Health.

17   Jamison quoted in Heather Benson, **Lethal Beauty. Saving a Life: the common assumption that suicide can't be prevented is wrong**, San Francisco Chronicle, 5 November 2005.

18   MHFA Guidelines, Suicidal Thoughts and Behaviours, www.mhfa.com.au.

19   Adapted from Rudd et al, **Warning signs for suicide: theory, research and clinical application**, Suicide and Life-Threatening Behaviour, vol. 36, 2006, pp. 255–62.

Graeme Cowan

Graeme grew up in Taree on the north coast of New South Wales. After coming to Sydney to study, he worked in sales and marketing management for Johnson and Johnson, and a division of Pfizer. His career then took a fork into recruitment and he worked for Morgan and Banks and then AT Kearney in senior management.

Despite an outward appearance of success, Graeme had been battling with depression since he was 21. The last episode, by far the worst, lasted five years. That extraordinarily difficult period resulted in four hospitalisations and a suicide attempt. He tried 23 different medications, ECT, Transcranial Magnetic Stimulation, cognitive behaviour therapy, and many alternative treatments.

Through much hard work and trial and error, Graeme gradually found a way of living that helped him to recover.

In the midst of his depression, Graeme felt alone and yearned for the real life examples of people who had recovered. This was to be the inspiration for *Back from the Brink* — stories of prominent and everyday Australians who have overcome depression.

Graeme speaks on many topics related to depression including lifestyle habits for mental health, how to support a loved one with depression, and managing for depression in the workplace. He also speaks on Brinkmanship: the art of turning adversity into opportunity.

He has two wonderful children and loves living by the bush in Sydney which contributes to his peace of mind.